God Is My Witness

Co-funded by the
Creative Europe Programme
of the European Union

Joshua Barley is a translator of modern Greek literature and writer. He read Classics at Oxford and modern Greek at King's College, London. His translation of Ilias Venezis' *Serenity* is published by Aiora Press, and his translations of the poet Michalis Ganas (with David Connolly) will be published by Yale University Press.

Original title: *Μάρτυς μου ὁ Θεός*

© 2013, Kichli Publishing
© For this edition Aiora Press 2019

ISBN: 978-618-5048-96-9

First edition April 2019

AIORA PRESS
11 Mavromichali St.
Athens 10679 - Greece
tel: +30 210 3839000
www.aiorabooks.com

MAKIS TSITAS

God Is My Witness

EU PRIZE FOR LITERATURE 2014

Translated by
Joshua Barley

AIORA

To my sister
Theodora Tzita
and to my editor
Belica-Antonia Kubareli

For God is my witness,
how greatly I long after you all
in the bowels of Jesus Christ.

St. Paul, *Philippians* 1:8

THERE ARE FOUR KINDS OF BOSSES: the successful, the indebted, the shits and the mad. My fate was the latter.

He would speak to me as if he didn't know if it were me standing there or someone who looked like me. I mean, if I were Chrysovalantis—employee and friend—or my twin brother. It's just, I don't have a twin brother. I have two sisters. If we happened to meet in the lobby, he would say, 'Don't lag behind!' and dash into the lift. As it went up he'd shout, 'No cheating!' and make me run up eight floors, counting aloud each of the hundred and forty-four stairs. From the lift he'd yell, 'Louder, fatty! Where's your spirit?'

His company closed in the late '80s and I became unemployed out of the blue. I had worked with him eleven years, but I was taken unawares. My other colleagues had done marketing work for a few months and they immediately went to other graphic design studios. I could see that the ship was sinking, of course, that things were going from bad to worse, that there was no future, but I didn't want to believe it. I had bought Old Nick's myth: 'Even if all the others go, there's no way you'll be left without work.' That's where I screwed up.

I saw myself wrestling myself in the mud. The one swore at the other and tried to suffocate him. All the while they were piously chanting the Kassiani hymn.

Then the two became one Chrysovalantis, whose name was Psychovalantis, and he shouted thrice, 'This wind is choking me!' The sound of an aria from *Tosca* came out of nowhere.

A strange dream.

I can't imagine myself as a beggar or a tramp. But nor can I imagine my parents falling victim to exploitation, particularly from a bride-to-be.

My father is now eighty-three years old, a retired officer, a family man, a man of letters and the Church. His is a quiet life. He has always looked after me, tended to my needs and loaned me money.

He would say, 'Careful, careful, careful!' but I was gullible and defenceless. My father was strict, but pliable. With a little pressure, he gave in. Yes.

'Dad, I'm going to London. Give me a hundred thousand, won't you?' He would.

'Dad, I have a small debt with the bank.' He would pay it off immediately.

'Dad, I have a problem, can you help me out?' He ran to my side.

'Dad, I have to be admitted to hospital.' He would help.

He never said no. Now that I think philosophically about it, his bark was worse than his bite. I hadn't realised that. I respect and admire him. Until I was twenty I was terrified of him. Afterwards I just respected him, since he had been through a lot. He is a man with life-experience. A father never wants harm to come to his child. He was glad that I always had ties to monasteries and churches—he's also a God-fearing man. All of my family are.

When, at eighteen, I entered the officers' academy at Trikala, he said 'well done', but when I gave it up (I couldn't take any more) he had no objection.

He never stood in my way. No.

Perhaps that's why I still haven't left home even though I've turned fifty. I feel safe and snug.

I called an old colleague to wish her happy birthday and see if she could give me some work. She hung up, saying, 'Chrysovalantis, you've caught me on my way out. Let's speak another time.'

You see, the lady has no need of me anymore. She's got a cushy job with the Athens 2004 Olympics and she's on two thousand a month plus bonuses. But the party won't last forever. Then let's see what happens...

Many of my former colleagues, who I had helped in countless ways, sneered at me when I asked for help. So did the businessmen at the small companies, who'd had me at their beck and call when I was working for Old Nick. Now they've lost their cream they pretend they don't know me. Oh well, I have faith in God. I wish them all well. That's a blessing from my priest: to be able to say 'I have faith in God' and 'thank you' even to those who wronged me. My conscience is clear. I listen to my priest as much as possible. He's told me what to do in my life, and how to cope so I don't end up in a loony-bin.

When you go bankrupt, you see how to get by without money. You want to get a free coffee. You want to sit somewhere and talk. I've done extensive research on penury.

That's why every Sunday morning, after the service in Agia Irene on Aeolou Street, I pass by the Anglican church where they serve coffee for free. If you go in and attend their service, they even give you a religious book for free. It's in English, of course. (I might not understand the language, but no book is lost on me.)

I try to get by on my wits. Yes.

My mother is a saintly being, a truly family-oriented, subservient woman—the rock of the house… but timid as a mouse. I remember her standing behind my father having put his food on the table, or laughing her head off in the cupboard while hanging up his ironed shirts, all alone. I looked at her with concern and thought, 'That's it, Mum's gone mad.'

My older sister is a professor of theology. She's a diligent, modest girl. She stood out among our whole family. Exceptionally studious. She has two degrees and still started a doctorate at fifty. It doesn't bother her that she's already spent four years on it and she's still writing. That old Plotinus will drive her mad. No personal life. Unfortunately.

My little sister is Chrysovalantis in female form. (I mean, the good features of my character, not the sordid ones.) Now she looks after the house. There aren't serious jobs for a sickly woman of forty-four. She's not going to work at a till. She'd get asked out by some bloke for coffee in the evening. In the good old days our father wanted to get her work in the public sector, but she refused. She's frugal, thankfully.

Yours truly says, 'Pity me, pity me!' My life is spread out on a vast field covered in hot red peppers. When I fall (always face first), I scald myself. That's my life— always landing in traps, thorns and nettles, without thinking that I'm barefoot. I always forget to wear shoes—even slippers, though I know beforehand-where I'm heading. Unfortunately, that's just who I am.

I have repented, however. God is my witness. I have repented bitterly for everything I have done. I want to leave it behind and start afresh.

I don't want lovers or good-time girls or prostitutes. I want to be close to God. And if He grants me a serious woman, then OK, I will happily enter holy matrimony. If he doesn't grant that and wants me to be a monk, that's OK, too.

I've put a lot of people aside because I saw that they had nothing to give. They're leaky buckets. Bottomless pits.

I want Him to hear me when I pray. Oh Lord, lead me not into temptation.

I want fewer friends, too. Few, but good—quiet, honourable ones who won't suffocate me. Not those who'd give you a gas mask with one hand and pump carbon dioxide into your face with the other. What do they expect—the mask to break and me to suffocate? That's what we've become. Unfortunately, that's the mentality of modern Athens. It doesn't let us balance our debts or our lives. I speak from bitter experience.

A friend of mine, a priest, once said to me, 'A faithful friend is a strong defence; and he that hath found such an one hath found a treasure.' Did we find friends and then abandon them? Did we find gold and pass it by in our quest for diamonds? A grave mistake. I did that, and I have repented. I did it knowingly and in full clarity of soul. I abandoned friends—young and old, clergymen and lay people—looking for diamonds. But where are they? Where?!

The palaces of the soul are incomparably superior to material ones. Material goods are desired by mask-wearing friend-impersonators. Real friends care about the treasure of the soul, and they will do anything to bring it to light, however well hidden it is. The others aren't friends, they're leeches, and the leech doesn't have such clarity of soul that he can choose a person with quality. A leech has no feelings, nor spiritual peace—not even a soft pillow to sleep on. His conscience is not clear. No.

I don't know. How can you talk about ideologies when we see that most employers (at least ninety percent) prefer foreigners, just to save a few coppers?

The whole of Greece has succumbed to a plague. Spiritually and materially. And Athens is even worse.

Mr I. and Mr T. always call me over and buy me a drink when they see me. They have fat wallets from their hefty pensions. Both of them own six or seven rentals. They see penniless old me and they buy me a drink. A few days ago, they said, 'Come over, Chryso-valantis. Have a drink,' and I burst into tears. I don't know why. Out of love, I suppose.

The other day, when they saw me again and called me over, I didn't sit with them, out of shame. I'm fifty years old. They can't keep buying my drinks. Look what Old Nick has driven me to…

After Old Nick I got two other jobs in the same field. (Graphic arts were still doing well in the '90s.) They didn't pay me, though, and a third that I found was far away in Koropi and it brought a rupture to my health. Korydallos-Koropi, Koropi-Korydallos. It was seventy kilometres aller-retour. In short, two and a half hours there and two back. Bus from Korydallos to Omonia Square, and from there another to the Markopoulos junction, and then a taxi to the industrial zone. The same in the evening. I got tired, exhausted, spent. I needed twenty thousand a month just for transport. I got to work at eight in the morning and stopped at seven thirty in the evening. By the time I got home it was nine thirty or ten. I often didn't even manage to have a shower: I would eat and fall asleep in front of the TV. Yes. 'A-Plus-Plus Publishing', a colleague said, 'means "Albanian Publishing"'. Most of the employees were Albanian. They didn't dare to speak, of course. They lived in some shacks around the area. Five or six in a room and they'd pay ten thousand each on rent.I worked my heart out (as I always do) for that company, but there was no recognition from the employers. Unfortunately. A lithographer, typographer, or typesetter from the '80s is now on the fringes—he has to do something else to survive. The most respectable people, with talent and experience, cannot find work today. Technology has swallowed us up. It's tragic. Waiters at depraved nightclubs find work, so do bouncers, grave diggers, pimps, opportunists, yuppies, foreigners—and not we who sacrificed ourselves for books. How many of us rejected marriages so that we could offer something to the Gutenbergian Art (as the Germans call it)?

I don't want to go to those houses of sin any more. I have repented, I have confessed and I now live a moral life. I am looking for a girl to marry. I am exploring my prospects. I might need to lose a few stone. Yes. I have sampled all the delights of life. I mean, I have such a huge range of experience of female bodies and behaviour that I want, God willing, to find a good girl, not some tart. I wouldn't tell my secrets to my wife, of course. When you tell her that kind of thing, she'll spit on you, even if she's immoral and has done the most depraved things herself. It's a question of ego: she says, 'After all your shipwrecks, you've come to me to drop anchor? In my harbour? Get out, scum!'

I want to find a woman who isn't a prostitute, no, but who respects me the way a prostitute respects men. Back in my youth, I went into a brothel and said to the madam, 'I don't have three thousand drachma; I have two and a half. Can I come in?'

'No.'

'Why not?'

'Because the woman who gets on her back has no price. Never forget that.'

She meant, I suppose, that the money you pay won't go to her.

My confessor says that I should stay away from prostitutes, firstly because they carry thousands of diseases, and secondly because if I don't stop, I won't be able to hold down a woman. I'll remain a layabout for life. Of course, that's not particularly easy, but he tells me I must give it a good try. I must always be vigilant.

> I cried unto the Lord with my voice; with my voice unto the Lord did I make my supplication. I poured out my complaint before him; I shewed before him my trouble. When my spirit was overwhelmed within me, then thou knewest my path. In the way wherein I walked have they privily laid a snare for me.

What joy it was when my little sister was born! I was six years old and my older sister ten. I wouldn't budge from her cot. I gazed at her and when she smiled my heart fluttered. I didn't want others to come near her. I became angry. The day she turned forty, we had a gathering of relatives and my father's colleagues. They had settled down in the sitting room and showed no sign of leaving. At some point I was so irritated I shouted, 'Leave her in peace! She's had enough! Look, you've made her cry!' And then, 'Don't you have your own homes to go to?' I got a slap from the back of my father's hand that almost dislocated my jaw.

Whenever I see a woman, I remember Eumorphia and think how dishonourably she behaved. That affair left its mark on me. A smear on my heart.

Once when I saw her in the street I wanted to be sick. I changed direction immediately. I felt disgust.

Great disgust. For myself, mainly. How low I had fallen! How can a woman take a man who is doing just fine and turn him into a piece of junk…?

I ran into the entrance of an apartment block and began to sob. I banged my head on the wall and shouted at myself, 'Idiot, idiot, idiot!' I don't have a clue how I got home. My psychiatrist, Mr Zalmas, increased my prescription, and I quickly calmed down.

I don't want to see her. I don't want to know her.

Your heart must be a fortress that doesn't allow any old whore to come and go. It's not right for a second-rate female to find the breach in your walls and sack your heart. We must bar our gates tenfold and ask, 'Who goes there?'

I bought a small cheese pie on Panepistimiou Street. I paid one euro and thirty cents. That's four hundred and thirty drachmas. Before the currency changed the same cheese pie would cost sixty-five drachma. Yet wages have completely frozen. What is the world coming to?

I used to be a closed book. I would never talk about myself or the things that mattered to me. For some time now, however, I have decided on a new, truthful path. I don't worry about speaking freely to my confessor. A close friend of my older sister, a particularly respectable woman, gave me that advice. She told me to tell my

confessor everything, because when you talk to him—
when you confess—it's like talking to God Himself.

That's why I like going to Mount Athos. You find
high-calibre people there. On my last visit, this rather
telling event occurred: on the road to Xiropotamos
Monastery, I met a young man who was a bit funny
in the head. He was penniless and hadn't eaten. You
could tell something was off.

'Friend, are you going to the monastery?' he asked.

'Yes.'

'Is it your first time, or do they know you?'

'They know me,' I replied, slightly bristling in case
the holy people saw me with this junkie.

'Can you put a word in for me so I can stay?'

I went into the monastery, straight to father
Zacharias, and told him the score.

'Let's go to the abbot.'

We appealed to the abbot. At once he declared,
'This man needs our help.'

They fed and watered him, and gave him a towel
and a bed.

Later the abbot summoned us both to the guest
quarters and gave us each a bunch of the best quality
grapes, and a spiritually edifying book to the young
man. He spoke to us about a whole range of interesting
and useful things. I stayed until the weekend, but the
young man stayed a dozen days, so I hear. When he
left they gave him money and bought his tickets to
Athens. That's the kind of charitable people they are.

That day, Father Nicodemus spoke to us about Heaven and Hell. He told us a story that I always keep in mind:

A monk spoke through prayer to a dead monk, and found out that the dead monk was in Hell. He was upset, and said, 'Lord, please show me what it's like in Hell.' And the Lord said, 'You will find out tomorrow.' The next morning He sent a worm from Hell into the monastery. The worm gave off such a bad smell that the monks were forced to change monasteries and go as far away as they could. The monk said, 'Is that what it's like in Hell, Lord?' And He replied, 'That is the smell of one worm. In Hell there are a trillion such worms.'

I like that story very much and I think of it often. Every time I think of it, I say, 'It's time to stop the tom-foolery. Why should I fall back into whoring? Why should I tell so many lies again and string my parents along?'

I have the impression that my respect for them is a little insincere. I should have given them more. They should see me made good at last, with a couple of grandchildren. They would love that.

But I feel I have the soul of a scumbag. That's why I'm so wracked with guilt. Still, I believe that God will help me make things better. Only God can. Yes.

The couple came in hand-in-hand and sat opposite me. A Pakistani man with a Greek woman. Hear ye: a Greek

woman, fresh as spring water, with a Pakistani bloke!
You couldn't make it up. I'm ashamed. So ashamed. For
Greek masculinity.

My older sister is introverted. Quite the opposite of
me. She isn't married. I can't hold it against her, since
at least she has a wage and a degree of dignity in her
life. If only I were the same. I will be very upset if she
goes off the rails. She is one hundred percent traditional: home-work, work-home. Nothing more. And
she reads. No coffees, shopping, etc. She's a quiet old
girl. I don't want wild sisters. No. I'm happy to look at
the wild, striking, modern ones, but when I'm at home
I become another person—a monk.

I've begged thousands of people for work. I realise that
times are hard, but I know which employers have financial problems and which don't. At one large bookbinder's in particular I see fewer Greeks every year,
and more and more foreigners. Forty percent of in-
sured workers in Greece are foreign… They get paid
nothing, with no overtime, and they say yes to anything. They do it for two reasons: firstly, to win the
trust of their bosses, and secondly, to get the Greeks
out of the way, who they think are their competitors.
Imagine! The foreigners think that the Greeks are their
competitors! That's what we've become!

Should I change my citizenship? I'm confused.

They called me a suck-up, they called me a hanger-on, they called me Old Nick's parasite. They thought I didn't know. Well, I knew all of it, but what could I do?

They said all that because we'd go out on Sundays, just the two of us (his wife gambled day and night). I accepted for two reasons: firstly, since I thought he might be shamed into giving me a bit of cash for overtime. Secondly, I thought I might get a promotion. It was useless. I gave him jam and he gave me back poison.

He would call me on Sunday morning and say, 'Come to Kifisia.' He wouldn't ask if I had something on or an engagement later, he would just say 'Come!' And I would come running. I had to change buses three times. He could have picked me up once, couldn't he? The bastard.

In summer we would go to the sea, and the mountains in winter. On the way we would talk about lots of (I must say) interesting things. But when he started blabbering about my sisters, I got riled. He would say that they were a burden on me, that I run around for them, without even a 'thank you' (of course, that wasn't true).

'It's like they aren't even ashamed, the old cows, that they haven't married and are a burden on you.'

'But all three of us are unmarried.'

'Well, why don't you have a threesome?' he said. I wanted to open the door and jump off the cliff.

He thought nothing of it—unfeeling creature that he was—and, as always, he said, 'Sing to me. Otherwise I can't drive properly.'

Every journey I sang for hours on end. I would begin with 'Wide Sea', then onto 'The Ballad of Maudthausen' and then 'If Only the Heart Had Locks' and 'Miaow, Miaow, Catty', 'My Hazy Mind', 'My Story, My Sin' and folk songs from the islands and rebetika. He would get stoked and step on the gas. My repertoire always ended with one request:

I'm gonna live free as a bird
Not some fool in a cage
Singing for a female canary.

I knew that he was dedicating it to his gambling wife.

Once when we were going to Marathon 'for a little ouzo', he requested 'I'm an Eagle with No Wings', and he revved so high that I panicked and said, 'Should I stop singing?' He replied, 'No, keep going. We're doing fine.' I said, 'Please, there's a tip-truck ahead and a lorry behind. How are you going to overtake?' But he harped on, asking for 'Strangers in the Night' and flooring it.

Not an inch of respect for my person. No.

Once, when we went out on Saturday instead of Sunday, I said to him, 'I want a haircut.'

'We're about to pass Kalamos, I'll take you to a good barber. You'll pay two or three hundred.'

'Two or three hundred? What am I, a goat? What sort of barber is that?!'

'Well, you didn't ask me earlier to book you an appointment in Kolonaki.'

He always made me feel awful. He had me at his beck and call from seven in the morning to eleven at night: a crushed, hungry donkey with baggage up to its neck.

One day—since he had tricked me into thinking we were friends—I went to him and said, 'Could you give me a fifty thousand advance for my little sister's operation?'

'Go to accounts,' he answered drily, without looking up. The accountant sent me to Givashit (his partner) and he (who was cast in the same mould) said, 'Fatty, we're down to our last penny.'

How many insults did I suffer, even in front of strangers!

Once we had the creative director of a large advertising firm in the office and were discussing her brochures. Old Nick came in and, just as I was telling her the prices, he said, 'Right, you've said enough. Now go and get us a coffee.'

You bastard, you have a man who's like a walking advertisement for your business (I saw dozens of clients every day) and you demean him?! And you tell the others that he's always getting everything wrong? It was a psychological issue, my doctor told me: he demeaned his employees to make his own shares go up. Then he can think, 'I keep this company going even with such useless people.' Still, he put up with

Mopface answering back and making fun of him—not to say that he didn't rather enjoy it. (I came up with the name 'Mopface', and it stuck. She had a spotty, drawn face, goggle-eyes and a crooked nose. She was one metre thirty, with her arms up). If a boss gets pleasure from a girl mocking him, you know there is a serious psychological problem.

'Mopface,' Mrs C., the cleaner, would say to me, 'is taking him through the eye of the needle.' That meant one of three things: either that she knew some secret of his; that he was a masochist; or that he was completely out of his mind. The soul of man is unfathomable.

I am so happy. As the days go by, my little sister is recovering more and more from her stroke. She has begun eating, and, more importantly, smiling.

Whenever I speak about my sister I become emotional...

God gave man two fundamental things: freedom and a healthy bodily. We know that man, as a rule, is born healthy. He destroys himself and brings diseases upon himself of his own accord. The jaws of sin are deadly, as St. Paul said. We create our own problems—bodily, mental and financial—because we have not given ourselves up to God. Why not? Perhaps we should refresh our principles and live a more natural life again? Ultimately, was man made to construct bombs and luxury cars—Mercedes, Jaguar, Rolls-Royce, etc.—or to cultivate his garden, read and write books and have discussions with learned people? (Sadly, such learned people are now on the fringes.)

Freedom of action, initiative, free will: those are number one. That's what Jesus taught us. That's what he gave us in the New Testament.

Snapshot from a Saturday morning at the Neon Café: Lovely girl, fresh as spring water, around twenty-five, going around with a seventy-year-old man. What does she want him for? Clearly to bleed him dry. Sure, there are women who like older men, but let's not have an age difference of more than thirty years... then it's a disease. It's gerontophilia. And he was a sprightly old thing. One hand on his espresso and the other on her behind. In a public place! That's what you call a dirty old man.

I might be of medium height, but I take care that my mind works. Studying helps a great deal. Unfortunately, because of my diabetes, I tire quickly. If I had a degree, everything would be different.

I have bought two exceptional books: *Visit of a Spiritual Father to a Sick Man* by St Nicodemus of the Holy Mountain and *On Prayer* by St Gregory of Nyssa, but I cannot read more than three pages at a time and that only with difficulty. When I go to bed at night, I feel overwhelming fatigue and I want to be quiet, relax, not have anyone talk to me, so that I can gently give myself up to Morpheus. I pray first, of course: I put my hand on my heart and say, 'God, keep my family under your roof and give me peace and quiet.' I want to find myself at last. When you find yourself, you understand who you are. You either come to earth, or you take off and say, 'Now I can fly on a glider, now I can skim like a hawk above seas and mountains without being killed.'

I just want to be calm and forget my anxieties— banks, jobs, Old Nick, Mopface, Euphormia and all of her riff-raff.

If I get married, I would like a woman of around thirty-five, modest and without whacky fashion sense. I'm not interested in that. I'm not interested essentially because I don't want her attracting all kinds of attention, and everyone saying, 'Look, the useless bloke bagged himself a hot bird who's got it all.'

I would prefer a French woman (most desirably, of course, a Parisian lady). I believe that Greek women suit French blood, just as Greek men suit French women. I would like it even more if we could be wed in Paris, but the costs are high. I also don't know if my parents could make the trip. The Russian church here, however, would be excellent: a hall decorated with flowers, two priests and a mellifluous female choir singing Russian hymns, Byzantine-style. After the wedding, an authentic, traditional festival with a band from the old homeland of Karditsa. We wouldn't draw it out too much, though: I would want to enjoy the bride, too. The same for her, no doubt. After all, I've made up my mind: I'm not going to bed with another woman until I marry. So what if I'm something of a monk? God sees everything, and when I get a big head, He punishes me. So what if I hold back a bit?

As my older sister once told me, 'Wear the clothes that fit you.' She was right. I can't wear size thirty-eight shoes, nor a general's stripes. I'm not a general, but nor am I a little child with little shoes.

I just want a normal life, like a gentleman from the '20s or '30s. With a warm and comfortable house. Made of stone. Preferably with a piano. We would sit together as a family and listen to the news on the radio. That time of day is sacred for me. We would eat in silence, as monks do on the Holy Mountain— the only difference that instead of our attention being on the monk reading his stories, it would be on the sober news presenter (and the impartial journalist). Information is sacred—even if it's become theatre in Greece, and bad theatre at that. It's show biz. Unfortunately.

I would have liked to live in the era of the great actors of the '60s: Dionysis Papagiannopoulos or Vassilis Logothetidis. I would have loved to be a neighbour of Georgia Vasileiadou, to sit on her veranda drinking coffee (her with her little scarf and ruby lipstick and me with my robe de chambre), her telling me stories and me begging the coffee not to end.

My older sister was always strict. When Eumorphia began calling, she grew irate. With her female intuition, she had realised that Eumorphia wanted to ensnare me in her net, and she tried to protect me. I couldn't grasp that, however. Love had muddied my mind. When I went to London to find her a house, her mother phoned my parents to ask for my number. I hadn't told anyone where I was going, so my sister found out from her mother and became incensed.

'They didn't know what you were doing there?! Why on earth do you need to find their daughter a house? What are you, their slave? Do you have cash to spare, Chrysovalantis? Have you gone completely mad?' she yelled down the phone. I didn't say a word.

I don't want to remember those painful moments now—those moments of all-consuming passion. I want to erase them from my mind.

My life has changed now, but many years revolved around whoring. I was always after beautiful women and I thought that I would get them. But it's not like that. The whole thing (now I've got it straight) needs great mastery, which I don't possess. I only have that ease if I'm paying for it. What's to blame? My appearance. I don't wear inviting clothing, nor perfume, nor do I have those kind of loose girlfriends who you have a nice conversation with and then they say, 'I'm exhausted,' and you offer to take them home in your car but then you veer off to a hotel and it's all fine and dandy. Well, in the state I'm in, I have neither a car nor the money for a hotel.

I had a dream about Mr Grigoris, my old boss at Anathesi. He really loved me: he let me leave early from work, he gave me pocket money and bought me sets for chess, backgammon and ludo. 'You're a child,' he would say to me, 'and children need to play. The teacher teaches, the leader leads, the shepherd shepherds and the child plays.'

I remember, just before he died, he came by our house and I secretly put twenty thousand in his pocket. He had had no work for a long time and he was living on a tiny disability allowance due to his cancer. He was once magnanimous himself, helping anyone in need.

When I think of him, I always say, 'Where are you Mr Grigoris, with your gags and japes? You taught me my trade,'—he was the most respectable craftsman in our field—'You taught me a lot. Where are you now?'

I took it hard when he died. I cried for days. Unfortunately, I found out a month late. It felt like someone had torn out my heart, that they took a part of me and left forever. Like a kite on Clean Monday that flies high, and you look at it proudly, and if the string snaps it doesn't fall but goes higher and higher and is lost from sight: well, just like that, some hand cut the string and Mr Grigoris left far away, forever. I want to meet him in the next life. It says in the Gospel that the just will rise up and sing before God. Would that we were both in the choir of the Highest, singing 'Hosanna' all together with the angels and the saints!

When I go to church I always mention him—'For the eternal rest of God's humble servant, Grigoris.'— and every time I feel the same twinge in my heart.

I think that to honour his memory I should not change jobs but should stay on the ramparts like a good soldier. I should keep close guard of the spiritual values I received from him, as a true disciple would. Just as a banker, when you have entrusted a valuable jewel into his safe-keeping, doesn't give it away but guards it like the pupil of his eye, so I, too, won't give away the things I gained from Mr Grigoris. I will keep them like a spiritual banker of typography and of Hellenic publishing activity.

I would like to have children for three reasons: firstly, because God said, 'Be fruitful and multiply,' secondly, to look after me in my old age, and thirdly, to bring joy to my parents. They crave grandchildren from their son. It's the only thing I can give them, since I haven't managed to give them any money in all my fifty years. Unfortunately. I've only given them sadness so far. Let me give them some joy at last.

I would like to have as many children as God grants me. If I had the financial capability, I could easily have three or four or five. I would need a large house where we could all live together, even when the children grow up, so they don't say, 'Alright, Dad, I'm off.' I haven't done that to my father and I wouldn't want the Most Merciful One to give me that bitter cup. I would like them to live with me and listen to the experiences of their mad dad—not run off. That would make me very sad. Unless I had money and sent them to study abroad. Then I would go once a month to see them. Afterwards they would return to the security of their father's house. A parent always wants his children beside him.

I would prefer boys to girls, because girls are harder to control. They run their fathers around. It's more difficult to keep a rein on a female than a male.

Yes, my life would be like a fairy-tale and we would go for endless walks along the huge boulevards of Paris. We would sit in the elegant cafés and restaurants, where there is absolute quiet. The French, you see, talk in low voices. They've got manners—they maintain formalities (even if they then slag you off behind your back). We would sit as a family in one of the lovely places of Saint Germain. I would order them whatever they wanted, then I would pay and leave a generous pourboire. Generally speaking, I would like my children to love me. Unselfishly.

It is crucial for a father to trust his children and not say, 'Oh, my child is waiting for me to die so he can inherit.' Unfortunately, many children send their parents to old people's homes, essentially so they can manage their property—not own it, of course, but manage it. To my mind, that's deplorable. I want my father's blessing.

God sees—since He made man, He leads and protects him. What would be the point of me taking my father's house and then some Ukrainian woman turning up and grabbing it from me in six months? It's a double crime—the crime of the amoral theft, but also the serious crime of profligacy. Well, I reckon I don't have much but I don't need much—God feeds me, protects me, and I try to get along OK. As the Russians say—and they're quite right—if you have no woman, no wine and no food, at least you should enjoy yourself. That's what I want from life: to enjoy myself. Nothing more. I also wouldn't say no to a spouse from England (preferably from London), since they make good, blonde children.

When I was younger I was owed some money from work. One day my father said to me, 'I'll go and get it tomorrow.' I didn't want him to, since my employers were rotters and I was afraid they would behave badly and give him grief—he was then in his pre-Parkinson's period, we were holding it back with pills and doctors. I told him not to go. He insisted, and it riled me. I slammed the door and left. In the end, though, he went, and brought me back the money. Now that's a father! Then I apologised. It was a lot of money, too: one hundred and thirty-five thousand, some years back. I went the next day to my confessor and I asked him, 'What should I do?' He said, 'Don't worry, God will forgive you.'

It's been a cause of great resentment in my life that this person (see, I deign to call him a person!), this Old Nick, wasted the best years of my life. My best eleven years—until the ship sank. With me on board.

I worked hours and hours there. I thought, and still think, that a good book is like good bread. Good bread needs good preparation, high quality flour, but most importantly good craftsmanship. The same goes for the making of books, which are spiritual food. It cannot be entrusted to a foreigner. But everyone employs them now—they're cheaper. So, if you go to a printer's, it'll be an Albanian taking the work from the client. The whole image of the company and the product suddenly falls. You cannot pass the work over to clueless people. Book production is traditional work. It used to be handed down the generations. Now things have changed in every sphere: the studios, the printers and in the bookbinders. It's tragic. You cannot have a sacred discipline, like that of book-making besieged by tribes of people who neither have nor will have—for at least a hundred years—any meaningful connection to books. They are plunderers. They came in to make a quick buck. But the book is not merely a commercial product, like a bra or a piece of bacon.

In his youth, my father was very proud to be a true officer. The top dog. When his health problems began, he forbade us visiting him in hospital. He felt like a wounded eagle and didn't want pity from anyone.

I don't think that in his hour of need I have served him well. When I said to him once, 'Father, I did nothing for you when I was young,' he replied, 'Don't worry, you're doing it now, when I have need of you.'

My first contact with the sin of prostitution occurred when I was about seventeen, in a brothel on the corner of Menandrou Street and Pireos Street, right opposite the bus stop. I saw an open window and a woman with her elbow on the ledge. There was a coffee cup next to her, and a potted flower in bloom. She made a gesture as if saying hello, and when she saw that she had aroused my curiosity, she said, 'Won't you come in for a chat?'

I longed to go, but I had my misgivings. In the end I went in with a racing heart. I had heard that brothels were paradise. I wanted to experience it. I wasn't so insecure then. I wasn't so fat.

A fifty-year-old woman opened the door, not the girl in the window. I knew that she was the so-called 'madam'. She was really very sweet, anyway. She took me to the room, where the girl was waiting. She was a lovely brunette. I was very embarrassed, but I let her undress me. I was under the impression that first we would wash and then we would do the things my friends had told me about. But she started stroking me endlessly and saying things I had never heard before. Unfortunately, it all came out before we had managed to do anything at all. I felt that she did it deliberately, to knock off work an hour early. I never went back.

The second time, I went to a house in Kolonaki, where Sonia and Jenny worked. Sonia was a shapely forty-year-old, with a bulging behind and warm lips. I really enjoyed my time with her. We did everything and we did it properly. I went back six times. Then she disappeared, and Jenny told me glowingly that Sonia had married and gone to Volos. A good client fell for her and took her away. I was sad but pleased that she had got out of the mire.

Then there was a tidy hotel with beautiful women on Satovriandou Street. As soon as I finished work, at five or six, I would go straight there, two or three times a week. *Straight to Judy, who had both knowledge and beauty.*

When I had money, I would leave a generous pourboire everywhere I ate or drank. That's why the waiters would look after me so well. Now I am a sheikh with no robe. I'm bust. I never thought I would fall to these depths. You'll tell me, of course, that my friend T. fell from being a director to seeking a daily wage.

I have never smoked. I never dared, because after I turned fifteen, each time I'd come home my mother and big sister would say, 'Come on, let's have a whiff of you.' How could I dare! My friends would offer me chewing gum and cologne, but there was no way I would risk it.

If only one could repent and find his old, good self. As is well known, we weren't born defective. We become defective as we go along. Man is like a car. You get it from the dealer all shiny and new, and everything is tickety-boo until it starts to fall apart, misfire, rust and its beauty fades. Man becomes a moving coffin, or a resounding gong, if his life goes awry.

I had some savings, but I fell into the trap of the banks—the trap that goes, 'Take these credit cards and do your worst.' I messed up. I got every single card and suddenly Old Nick went bankrupt. I never imagined that things would come to this, that I would be out of work for two years. That's when I took my turn for the worse. Then I changed jobs three times in two and a half years. I already had all my outgoings, though: clothes, restaurants, lessons in Byzantine music, foreign travel, Eumorphia's rent for half a year and her housing costs—and, of course, medication and health-care for my father and sister (that, however, was from a debt of love).

How can I pay my debts now? I'm forced to hide. My phone rings and I don't pick it up. I feel like I'm on the run from the law. It's worrying.

I look frantically for work and I grow tired and even more worried. But then, work is like a hare. Was a hare ever caught without lying in wait?

A psychiatrist friend said to me yesterday that he would like to become acquainted with Old Nick and interview him. He thinks he would be a worthy case study. A rare kind of schizophrenia, studied by very few. I gave the doctor all the legal threats I'd been sent by him, and he told me that this person is a special case, one very rarely encountered.

Before Old Nick, I was at the electricity board. I was put there—in an excellent position, to give me a leg up—by Nikos, a distant relative of my mother's. A wonderful person of rare moral stature and refinement. I felt secure at his side. I had wings.

One day I phoned his office to speak to him and they said, 'I'm afraid Mr Nikos has passed away.' The receiver fell from my hand. I felt like a ship whose anchor cable had snapped. I went into the street and wandered aimlessly until dawn. Then I was sick with worry about finding a new sponsor at the board. I didn't find anyone, so when my contract ended, they didn't renew it and I lost not only my job but also my lovely office.

My life is sin and great tumult. I think that when I die I would like my tombstone to read

> *Here lies God's servant Chrysovalantis,*
> *Hounded by women,*
> *Loyal servant of the typographic industry,*
> *And lover of beauty.*

You cannot make a writer mop the stairs. That's ridiculous. In Australia there is a government department which decrees, 'He who has studied such-and-such can only work in such-and-such a job.' In Greece we have nothing like that. Here, some bloke will get into the public sector simply by finishing high school, and some wench will become the secretary of a fancy minister. Why? Because she wears a thong. Hang on, darling, what did you study to get that position? What have you read—or written? Even if I had a degree, I wouldn't go into the public sector because I like competitive work. The marketplace. I'm a fighter, not some worker bee.

Ultimately, our minds dream up everything to satisfy the flesh. Still, it's not pleasure that's the problem, it's extravagance. Excess. It's one thing to take your time over a lovely sauvignon blanc, and to enjoy it, and quite another to down three bottles of wine and turn into a raisin.

My father's mother, Grandma Chrysovalantia, was a cripple—the Holy Martyrs punished her. She had bought two candles, to light one each in the churches of the Virgin and the Holy Martyrs (for my father's health, which was ailing because he'd been dismissed from the army). Without thinking, she lit them both in the first church. When she went out into the courtyard, she realised what she had done and she returned to get one of them. But the Martyrs punished her: she tripped in front of their icons and remained crippled for life.

She lived in our home village, but we brought her often to Korydallos and she would stay with us for days. She was a very good woman. She had been through a lot—cancer, diabetes, heart problems. In the end she died of a stroke. A sweet person, she would sit in bed all day long, knitting and singing. She knew a lot of good Greek folk songs, and she taught them to me. She had a sweet voice and lovely big blue eyes. Unfortunately, I didn't take after her in the latter. She loved me dearly. She knitted clothes for me, and gave me chocolates and sweets: I was a gourmand from an early age.

Women love their illegitimate children, just as a thief loves his stolen goods. They say that illegitimate children are cleverer—like mongrel dogs, which are the best at hunting. I don't know.

When I did my military service, my father arranged for me to work in the Ministry of Defence. There, Mrs K. told me that I needed to flirt with women if I wanted to enjoy myself. I heeded that advice and became friendly with many lady soldiers. For the first time, I saw my shyness disappear into the cupboard, and I said, 'Women, women, women!'

I saw fully-grown colonels, bedecked with stripes, tongue-tied in front of women—'I mustn't upset her, she's particularly close to the general and if she wants, she can tell him the worst things about me and ruin me'—and they would tiptoe around her.

Tatiana was this sort of case. She was the lady officer who called the shots in the minister's office. We were all terrified of her—she was gorgeous and all the rest. She set her sights on me. Well, I knew that man is the hunter and woman the quarry, but this was the first woman I had ever met who was the exact opposite: she was the hunter and I was the quarry. She was forty-one and I was nineteen (I had just given up military school, to my father's great chagrin).

The lady officer was all chummy at first and she took me under her wing. She brought me into her home, where I met her husband (also an officer) and their two children. Then I realised that she had taken me there to pull the wool over their eyes: to make me friends with all of them, like an older son. At some point, she pounced on me in the sitting room. Since I respected her husband, however, I retreated and thought it best not to go there again. Every time she saw me in the Ministry she would take me to one side and say, 'Why are you avoiding me? I'm only trying to help. When will you come for a coffee?' A classic female, ready to give everything during sex. She came across as very feisty.

I stopped visiting her house, but we carried on going out, without doing anything too naughty— a bit of kissing and flirting. I was concerned that if we went any further she would start behaving strangely in front of my parents. I was certain that she was after something. They all are. They don't speak. They don't utter a word before sex, but as soon as it's over, before they've even got dressed, they ask you why you had intercourse with them, and you don't know what to say. She couldn't stand my parents. I realised after a couple of hints she dropped. She wanted to take me away from them. She wanted to install me in her family home in Thebes and fence me in—perhaps so I would look after it for her, water the garden, etc. She had the financial capacity to do that, and she really fancied me. She didn't want my money—on the contrary, she took me out and bought me presents. Basically, she liked to transgress for an hour a week. She enjoyed breaking out of her routine. It gave her a thrill. She liked my youth and my style, and she loved it when I told her stories. It would turn her on. 'How beautifully you speak,' she would say, feeling me up.

I would be talking or eating and she would be feeling me up. I was more sprightly then. I would say, for example, 'My chest hurts,' and she would immediately reach under my shirt.

She was a full-blooded and passionate woman. Once, when I was taking some envelopes to her office, she pounced. She slammed the door and, before I knew what was happening, kissed me forcefully on the lips. I didn't squeak. At that moment I felt cleansed, like I was having a lovely, refreshing wash. Like I was in the muck and the slime, and a real sponge from Kalymnos, doused in some fragrant soap, had come and cleansed me of everything. Yes.

Despite that, I didn't go further with her, perhaps because I felt that she had the upper hand in everything. I didn't like that at all. She had completely appropriated me and made me a tool. She would say, 'We'll go here, we'll go there' (she was a very good driver and had a nice car): to a fish restaurant in Eretria, to Vari for pork chops, etc. She usually picked up the bill, but I also had some money (from my father). I liked this, but it suffocated me. I wanted freedom, independence and a healthier relationship, with a younger, unmarried girl.

I know that she still loves me and thinks about me, the proof being that every year on my birthday I receive a bouquet of red roses—as many as the years of my age. I know that in the state I'm in, if I call her and say, 'Tatiana, blah blah blah,' she would bend over backwards for me—she might even find me work. She's now seventy, her husband has died and her children have married. She'll want company. But I rarely call her. It's immoral. I have to learn to bear my cross.

Life has taught me that at some point, come what may, we will all bear our own cross. It's better, therefore, to do it standing up straight. And it's better now that I have mental and physical strength.

God guides His people. He decrees what is right and wrong, and He bestows complete freedom, complete self-determination. Besides, He says it expressly in the Gospel: We were born free. That's why you see the monk, a healthy and happy man, saying, 'I'm going to take up my cross.'

And now, how do I relate all this to Tatiana? The last thing she wanted was to see her son become a monk. 'What if he begs you?' I asked. 'Over my dead body,' she replied. Yet in my case, she wanted to lead me away against my will.

I've been involved with labour costing for a long time. And a good friend of mine deals with all kinds of work issues. We sit down together and say, 'Can you believe that in one café in the Pedion tou Areos park, two out of the three waiters are foreign? Is that the image we want to project for the Olympic Games? Is the French athlete, the Swedish interpreter or the English journalist going to be waited on by a Russian and a Kurd? What will his reportage say when he returns to London? That the Greeks have forgotten their Greek? That the Greeks don't have a word of English? Is that what the Europeans will say about us? Come on, let's get a grip.

I am certainly going to find another confessor, because this one just turns his back when I say hello. Either that or I'll find a nice little job in London. That would be fine. I'd get a house for me and my little sister. I struggle on. I pray. Anyway, there is no world without temptation.

I want my sister to recover completely. That is the best present that the Lord could give. I'm her protector. I care for her. I love her. Even her husband (let's hope she marries) couldn't be as close to her as me. When you have known her for forty-four years, and, of course, when you're of the same blood... I went on my knees to Saint John the Russian for my sister. 'Oh wondrous saint', I said, 'heal her completely and guard her for years to come.'

I was all at sixes and sevens when we went to London for her epilepsy. It was all I could think about from morning to night. I called our parents every day: 'It's all fine, all fine,' I would say, so they wouldn't be upset. I suffered alone. Thankfully the hospital was very good: the doctors were excellent and the nurses were obliging. I stayed in a hotel nearby. There was a very nice Welsh lady working on the reception—about forty-five, not beautiful but very diligent and agreeable. I spoke to her about my problems and she was moved. I told her that I have hope and trust in God. She cried, even though her beliefs are somewhat heterodox, being an Anglican. We spent three days of anxiety, unease and pain. In the end, however, the operation was absolutely fine and now she has fewer fits. Glory to You, oh Lord.

A brothel woman, probably with no documentation, lives an unbearable life. In most cases she cannot escape the hands of pimps, nor the police. I loved going into their rooms and watching them undress, but at the same time I was overtaken with feelings of humanity: I would talk tenderly to them and kiss them sweetly all over, and at the end we would even have a chat. A couple of them became familiar with me and would say, 'When are you coming back?'

They are God's creatures, simply trying to grant contentment and orgasms to everyone. What an effort! A prostitute must placate the male impulse, almost like a conjuror, after the initial crescendo that invigorates the penile blood vessels, followed by the issue of sperm and then orgasmic collapse. All of that in a short space of time, and with thirty or forty people every day in different ways. This isn't beans or toilet paper we're talking about, which you can just go and buy at the supermarket...

These women are also the image and likeness of God. My feelings towards them: tender. They offered me pleasure and joy with open arms, and they always treated me well. Even now, in the state I'm in, whenever I see one in the street, she will speak tenderly to me. Not like Eumorphia, Roro and all those others who have treated me so badly... If the money I had thrown at those 'women' I had spent on prostitutes instead, I would have enjoyed myself so much more and kept my inner peace.

The only downside was the filth. Twenty people might have gone into that bed in one day, without having washed their feet; there might be lice on the pillow; someone with a fungal infection might have wiped themselves on the toilet paper. Therefore, I would always go to the pharmacy afterwards and buy anti-lice, pharmaceutical shampoo. I would return home, go straight to the bathroom and wash myself for a long while.

I used to go to the brothels on Fridays and Sundays, usually in the evening. I once went to a Romanian called Delia, and I told her the story about Eumorphia. She said, 'Don't worry, you can come and vent to me.' I calmed down. I visited her twice more, but then she changed her spot: she was taken to Rhodes, they said. Delia had what I was after: the caring eye of a mother. I always wanted my women to have that look. I wanted my prostitute to understand my mental state and my needs and to behave first as a mother, then as a friend, then as a lover and finally as a copulating female.

Jesus saith unto them, Verily I say unto you, that the publicans and the harlots go into the kingdom of God before you. For John came unto you in the way of righteousness, and ye believed him not: but the publicans and the harlots believed him: and ye, when ye had seen it, repented not afterward, that ye might believe him.

Every time a woman made an advance on me, I thought she was a gift from God. 'This is fate,' I would think: she has come to give me something, not to take. I thought of her like a flower that, once picked from the garden, is only fragrant for a few days. That's what love is like: after sexual intercourse it loses its scent. The second time is never like the first. That's why the Omniscient One gave women the hymen—their virginity—so they would remember which man they fell into the bed of carnal relations with. Since I never had the fortune—the honour, I would say—of sleeping with a virgin, every time I went whoring I would choose a different one, so I could fantasise that, since she was new to me, she was a virgin. They didn't realise that, though, and they thought that something had gone wrong and that's why I chose another.

I know a married priest who hangs around with transvestites. He goes to their homes. He tells me that he does it to try to bring them onto the straight and narrow. If that's the case, good on him. But when the tenants of the block see him going into the apartment of a transvestite, who just before had been selling her (his?) wares on Syngrou Avenue, what are they to think? Wouldn't they naturally be scandalized?

'We love our fellow man with all of his faults… No one is perfect. We grew up in the Church and we know that only through Her can lost souls be saved,' he says to me with tears in his eyes. On the other hand, yesterday I heard that he was seen going into a gay bar in Thessaloniki without his cassock on. Make of that what you will.

I think that if I had money and a good woman who entertained pure and sincere feelings for me, I would whisk her away and go to live in some civilised country. For apart from the Saints, who watch over us, there is nothing of any value in this place: so the fathers from the Holy Mountain say, too. Our civilisation has fallen into the hands of uncivilised, godless and barbaric people. Better London, Paris or Australia—at least, somewhere with Greeks. Love your fellow Greek outside of Greece—he won't do you any harm. And hate the Russian in Greece—he will.

It's not on for a priest to say, 'You're making your life a brothel!' He thinks I don't listen to him, that my behaviour isn't correct, that I'm whining at him. Mate, it's a confession: I am lamenting my sins. However strict you are, if you decide to go into ministry, show some understanding. Otherwise do something else.

'I ban you from taking communion!' he shrieked heartlessly. The whole church must have heard him. I resented that.

I immediately thought of changing confessors. I want someone who I can talk to and who will listen patiently and with kind intentions. You'll tell me that a confessor isn't a psychiatrist, but still, he should have some uplifting role that abates human frustration. A confessor should find a way to communicate with you, to open the doors of your soul in a couple of minutes. That way you will trust him. For you speak to God through the priest.

I had that strict confessor for six years, but I realised that he was the same as the previous two, the tyrants. I long to get away from him and find another, better one. Who knows, maybe I'll become a priest myself one day. Then I'll be able to say that I am offering something to society. I would feel the glory of Byzantium inside me and spend my free time learning Byzantine music and foreign languages—particularly English and French.

I wrote a poem about a girl who hurt me—I mean, really hurt me.

> *I climbed a mountain with you*
> *To show you how much I love you.*
> *I got exhausted, worn out and dazed*

I asked you for a couple of sips of water
But hot wine was all you gave.

Footnote: 'hot wine'. I wanted a drop of cool water, but she gave me hot wine to burn me and make me drunk—to keep me in a permanent lethargy. A lethargy of despair and insecurity.

If a woman ever gets involved with an intelligent man, she enjoys creating a constant state of insecurity in her subsequent lovers: the notorious 'female vengeance'. She's been with a clever chap and it's gone seriously wrong—she didn't manage to ensnare him as she wanted—and so she looks around for other people who are not at fault in any way, to get what she was deprived of.

I have been faced with this myself. The ancient saying came into my head: 'eros is overcome by eros.' So, to forget her, I tried to find another: for I really believed that I would never again come across such horror. And yet, it happened. Indeed, the 'last error proved worse than the first', as it says in Matthew. I came a cropper. Yes.

All of this drove me to gluttony, drunkenness and the cafés of expensive hotels, comfortable as an English gentleman's club, with soft music, leather sofas and well-mannered waiters who tread soundlessly, their polished leather shoes sinking into the spongy carpet. I would place my order as if I were one of their dignified patrons. I would drink my whisky slowly and plunge my hand sensually into the deep, nut-filled bowl. But now I have repented for all of that. Pitifully. God is my witness.

A woman is like the fire brigade. When she sees a man in flames, she should know how to put him out and save him. But usually she leaves him to burn.

Hear ye, my experience of fifty years and three months, with grey hair and a diminished brain. My brain was not sold, alas, but put under the hammer.

My Aunt Dionysia is a strict but level-headed woman. She was infuriated by the Eumorphia affair. She would rail against her from morning to night, along with my big sister. 'Get away from her!' they would say. It was her bullying, scrappy style that annoyed them.

'Beware, Chrysovalantis! She doesn't look like a professor's daughter. She didn't learn any principles at home. And yet you're the very image of a colonel's son.'

'Aunt, you heard it from me: she has a secret life!' my older sister added.

And look, they were right. I don't know how this happens. Some women have such a well-developed instinct. Even though they only met her once, they were spot on. Of course, I was an idiot with Eumorphia. A cretin. I was like the mouse that dips not only its tail but also its head into the burning oil.

I'm trying to change now. Now that I'm penniless, too. My dream is to see Chrysovalantis in a job and with a woman. A girlfriend. Not some Russian or Bulgarian: a Greek, to please my parents. When you grow up, you wonder if the eggs you laid turned into birds, or if the incubation failed.

My parents want me to marry but they don't say so—they are afraid that if they say so I will bring home some wretch. They drop hints: 'So many female suitors!' they say. For now I am the female and they are the male. Neither a psychiatrist nor a confessor can understand my state of mind. They say I have a female character: I don't react like a male. The male always has a shade of aggression, while the female is passive. I mean, instead of being the fist, I'm the punch-bag. They say that I grew up in a molly-coddled environment until I was ten. They're right: grandmothers, money, presents and high-ranking officers and clerics.

I thought I was living in Paradise—a huge children's playground. Everyone knows that a person's character is formed before he is seven. According to American researchers, if a child doesn't see crime on the television before he is ten years old, there is no chance that he will ever commit a crime. All will be good and healthy. No problem. Yes.

I thought I was in a castle, that the drawbridge came up every evening and that I was completely safe. I was what they describe as 'in my own world.' Since I was a babe I thought that I lived in a society of refined gentlemen—a Parisian community, with English elegance. A grave error. I don't forgive myself for it. I was nobility—my word was my promise, my appearance impeccable. Then, when I was in London for my sister's treatment, an Englishman said to me, 'Beware of men with silk ties.' He was quite right, but I realised that too late. People with ties aren't always gentlemen, nor friends.

I believed in society as it was at the time of Victor Hugo, Shakespeare, the King Louis', Queen Victoria. Not that I am a royalist, but I considered—and still consider—the structure of our family to be royal in nature: dad is the king, mum the queen, my big sister is the older princess, I am the prince and my little sister is my little princess. I thought that we'd all get on well without deceiving one another. I believed in another era. I grew up with bishops in their magisterial, priceless golden robes, and I would say to myself, 'That will be me one day. I will become Chrysostom or Athenagoras. Mum, go and get your old flowery hat.' And I would wear it. 'Grandma, I'm hungry,' I would say, and my grandma would bring me whatever I wanted. She never let me down. I dreamed of that kind of society and I find myself in an Amazonian jungle of delusion. I was sure that when I was thirty I would have fairy-tale comfort (of the highest aristocratic style), that I would have a boat with wheels that would become a Bond car as soon as it emerged from the lake. I believed in that kind of life.

I went to a café on Acharnon Street, where they do a good espresso and where the waitress is a redheaded beauty from Mesolonghi. She wasn't there, unfortunately. They fired her and took an Albanian—what else?—in her place. They already had two: one at the buffet and one washing up. Three out of five there are Albanian. That's what they're like: they support each other and fight tooth and nail to cling to their jobs. They're afraid that if they go back to Albania, the mafia will catch them and tell them to hand over the money they made in Greece or they'll chop off their heads. That's why they're trying to settle here. Some even get married. In a short while we'll have a huge survival problem: the Greeks will become Chinese porters carrying Albanian tourists.

If we go on like this, there'll be a lot of crime, on a large scale. My big sister agrees on this. It's time that the Greek police thought about it. I mean, do five hundred purses a day need to be snatched for the state to wake up? Must the Russians and Pakistanis and Senegalese suffocate us in Athens before we see the light?

Unfortunately, today's Greek doesn't even love the Church, the country or his family.

God have mercy.

My relationship with my new confessor, Father G., is excellent and healthy. I see him whenever I want. He always has time for me. He's a good person and I believe that he has the fear of God in him. When a priest has the fear of God (that's a gift, no question), he's not a professional, he's a treasure trove. A friend of mine who has been under his guidance for many years introduced us. He brings me peace and solutions to my problems.

When I spoke to him at some point about Eumorphia, he said, 'Stay away!' He told me to wipe her completely from my mind and never call her again—also to pray every day and to try to eat less. Food plays its part in sexual desire. Your ego gets involved, and you say, 'I loved her, I did this that and the other for her, and she...' Food is oil on the fire.

I also asked a priest from St Panteleimon (the Russian monastery on the Holy Mountain) about it, without going into too much detail, and unfortunately his reply was the same: 'Get away and save yourself. Find another woman.'

When a priest puts his stole over my head, I feel that I am coming into contact with God. That's the goal of the Mysteries. If you lie in confession, it's like lying to the Holy Spirit. A clergyman has no reason to misguide me.

I am worried when I get a call at home. My mind immediately goes to my little sister, whose health has wavered yet again. I see her suffering and my heart bleeds. Today I went to see the doctor who looks after her and we had a chat. He is cautiously optimistic. I also went to another for a second opinion, and tomorrow I have an appointment with a third. He was hitherto assistant director at the renowned University Hospital of Rome, I was told. In the morning I will go to do her insurance papers. I don't mind tiring myself out as long as she is OK. I don't know if I'm a good person, but I know that I'm a good brother.

My first love, at the age of fourteen, was Eleni from Agia Varvara (5 Lysandrou Street). She told me she was fifteen, even though she was eighteen (I was informed too late of that, as well). Her brother was a butcher. A neighbour of hers would say to me, 'Get out of here, you scumbag, there's no way she'll let you kiss her. And if Pentelos gets wind of you, he'll chop you up with his cleaver.'

I panicked and fled.

This girl got me down for six or seven months. I would disappear from home for hours on end. I went to a café opposite her house, where gypsies gathered, and they would say, 'Scram! Pentelos will call the police.'

Those were good years.

Next was Jenny (*Jenny Jenny, better than any*) and then Litsa (*Litsa Litsa, can't I kiss ya*) and then Judy (*with the lovely booty*). I always loved girls. No confessor-surgeon could heal my wound: there always remained a serious inflammation. I believed that women were good spiritual beings, like me. As I grew up, therefore, I became an easier victim. What do they want? Do they want me to admit I'm useless?

This is the point we have reached as Greeks. You see our women on the arms of Arabs, Russians and Albanians. What will they say to their parents if they see their daughter with a foreigner and don't know what his background is? Has he jumped jail in Tirana? Is he a hit-man for the Russian mafia? Unless, of course, the girl's father is himself a dirty old man going around with a Russian babe, in which case he wouldn't care.

I think that we're seeing a gradual takeover of Greece. And this time they're not breaching the walls. Is Greece voluntarily preparing herself for surrender? Will the formal ceremony of surrender be the opening ceremony of the Olympic Games? We've thrown open our gates—have we opened the abyss, too?

Are we heading for shipwreck? At least if it comes gently, we'll cope. But I'm afraid that those in charge are planning to hurl us onto the rocks and the jagged precipices. Yes.

I look at myself in the mirror and I see that my hair has become cotton—thanks to the stress and depression. Of course, thanks to age as well. I've knocked back fifty years now. I start to think deeply: youth cannot be taken back, just like swear words, rocks and money.

My mother used to tell me, 'Be careful of women. They're gossips, liars, snatchers and they're always staying out late. Beware. You are an innocent child, brought up on principles… If you get involved… they'll eat you for breakfast.' Some time I'd like to ask her why she's so afraid. But if a mother is afraid, the child is afraid, too.

My life now feels like a cracked cup which won't be glued back together for anything. I was a diligent student and I loved school, but my first contact with typography made me renounce letters and follow the art of printing. I was progressing well until about fifteen, and then my mind started to wander—going out with friends, kissing girls, etc. The truth is that my teachers didn't treat me well: they considered me a Vlach and a peasant (they nicknamed me 'the Shepherd'), since I was the only pupil who had come from Karditsa. It was unfair, since being a Vlach and a peasant means neither that you're bad nor uneducated, especially when you have manners and principles and have been enlightened through your family's cultivation—something that is evidently absent these days. (The first person who'll give you food and a slap is your mother —and milk, of course. Warm milk from her breast, converted by her organism from blood into that lifegiving white essence. Great is the mystery...)

Anyway, I abandoned my studies and directed myself seriously towards the art of typography. A beautiful and enviable art, but I was lacking university distinctions: more, I suppose, since I saw my two sisters get degrees. Yes. How different everything would be if I had a degree as well.

Until a man reaches forty, he remains a carefree and frivolous child. After forty he starts thinking seriously about himself and his retirement. My parents urged me to study, but in vain. There were jobs in the private sector then and everyone was quite blasé. 'He didn't qualify for the public sector, nor the military,' they would say, 'but he'll find a job.' Now that there is so much unemployment the difficulties have struck. I see endless cucumbers sown in my garden, and I didn't plant them. Who, I ask, was the invisible gardener who went into my garden on the sly, not to steal and destroy my plants, but to sow cucumbers, hot peppers and stinging nettles?

Athenian women, instead of buying an edifying book, by thongs and lipstick from department stores, so that some Arab, say, can lick his lips. They're no different from the prostitutes of London—yes, I saw them when I was there. The lady's wearing all lace and has everything on display. Then some chap introduces himself and he's all over her with the first 'Nice to meet you.' It's a natural consequence: she provokes it. She likes to cause a stir with her beauty. And then she goes on TV and says, 'I was raped.' Sorry, who are you to say you were raped? You're asking for it. That's why they say there are three kinds of women: the modest, the beautiful and the sensationalists. The modest ones are those who dress in accordance with their principles, which are perfectly respectable. They don't wear tight trousers, they don't pluck their eyebrows, they don't smear themselves in paint. The beautiful ones have natural beauty. Your eye is instinctively attracted to them. The sensationalists are the unnatural development of the species. Their aim is to provoke men. And we're to blame, for we haven't understood that all that glitters is not gold. We mess up. Just like I mess up every time. Just like any respectable Mediterranean man messes up.

A Russian woman tried to get her hands on my money, but she didn't succeed—I was alert to it. We had met through Marinaki and were supposedly friends. Just the third time we met, she said, 'Could you lend me thirty thousand drachmas?' Well, you can't give what you don't have. (To be honest, if I had it, I might have made the error.)

They say that Russians are romantic. I don't dispute it. Perhaps they were once. I absolutely believe, however, that most of them now are opportunists, trying to exploit every legal loophole to shore themselves up and take on a pro-European identity. Not European but pro-European. That way they can play on three tableaux at once: firstly, to be former citizens of the once-powerful Soviet Union; secondly, to belong to a place of progress and human rights; and thirdly, to come and go to our country any time they like. That's their fundamental interest. I speak from experience.

At heart, I'm afraid of myself. My doctor and confessor are afraid, too. Their hearts tremble with mine. I'll be honest: I'm like a candle. As long as I'm away from the fire, I keep my self-confidence intact. But if I go near it, I melt. I'm afraid that they will ensnare me again with their sweet talk and I'll relapse. I swear to myself that if the Sirens come, I will, like a new Odysseus, seal my ears tight. I draw courage from this. But, as my Grandma Chrysovalantia said, 'Fill your belly up with food, but don't let your head get too big.' That's what worries me. If they catch me in their nets, I might relapse. If I earn some money again, I might be a fool. You never know with me.

Since they've taken me for a ride so often, they'll do so again. My confessor says this outright. Don't go there! And I follow his advice to the letter. He is an excellent priest, he loves me and really cares for me. He has shown great understanding. He always says, 'Stay away! Get out and save yourself. There's no chance a model will look at you. You're neither a model nor a sugar-daddy, Chrysovalantis.'

My psychiatrist friend also stressed this: 'Dear boy, women read us chapter and verse. But have you ever read a woman?'

I like monasteries. Particularly those of the Holy Mountain. (How wonderful and poetic its characterisation as 'The Garden of the Virgin'!) There you find all the spiritual and material culture that makes you feel proud of our ancestors. You find fantastic libraries in which generations of monks have copied manuscripts.

They did that all their lives, copying old codices. They had a blessing from an elder to do nothing else but this.

I couldn't be a monk. I couldn't leave my family to hole myself up in some quiet monastery. Who would look after them? Moreover, I love monasticism but fear that I wouldn't manage to follow the strict, ascetic life. Ultimately, I don't see it as a solution. God doesn't simply accept someone because he's failed professionally, has never grown up, is drowning in debt and now clings to the plank of monasticism. God can't abide that.

I feel like a failure, even though my confessor says that I need to get over it. 'Don't look for self-affirmation from women or money, my child.'

The truth is that at fifty years of age, a woman is yet to give me a chaste kiss—a kiss with pure feeling. Don't think, mind you, that I am completely oblivious and expect to find love in my flowerbed and pluck it like a gardenia. But I do know how they treated me when I was financially comfortable, and see how they ignore me now. Yes.

My love for the Byzantine music of Russia grew by leaps and bounds when I met a Russian with quality— Mr F., a principled person, an authentic Muscovite and distant descendent of the Romanovs. He was nothing like the Russians we all know, who merely used him to broaden their clientele. I went to him for singing lessons. I paid him, of course.

Music has always interested me. When I pray, I like using Byzantine hymns, while in my personal moments I reach the same tenderness through other melodies. Of course, I recognise the danger of being permanently in a state of deep sentimentality.

I am a vibrating, taut string which might produce sound but also might snap—I don't know. I feel this often, and unfortunately the ladies smell it and come near me like a bee to honeysuckle. Yes. They think I am an open book and that they will be able to squander my last euro, unimpeded. But they're wrong. When they discover how poor I am, they say, 'Chrysovalantis, let's meet some other time,' and they wait for the piggy-bank to fill up again. Women have a knack of knowing if a man has money in his pocket — Russian women in particular, who are expert in finance. I don't know, perhaps that's a consequence of the penury that was rife in their country. When the state leaves you poor, you try to find an escape. You look to see where the money is and how you can get it quickly, exploiting some loophole as a pretence.

They are exceptionally artful. The Madame will arrange a meeting, but what's her intent? To skin you and not let you even touch her knee. On the other hand, it's not right for me to ask for money from my sisters in order to give it to a foreigner. It's dishonourable. I have a conscience, you know. If you buy her even so much as an orange juice she'll be happy: she'll be able to say she got something from you.

These are the so-called 'neo-misers'. It's a serious matter. Yes.

> *O Tsitsornia,*
> *The vultures are all awaiting ya*
> *Kalinka, Kalinka, Kalinka moya*
> *If you don't take care, they'll take your underwear*

I take care. I take great care. I take care not only because I have nothing, but because I'll need to take care in the future, too, when I *will* have something.

It's highly fortunate that I met these latest Russian women (long after Marinaki) when I no longer had any money. It's highly fortunate, yes, and I thank God for it. Otherwise I would fall apart. Straight to the psychiatrist. This isn't the real solution for a (yes, I'll use that harsh word) loveless person.

Foreign women have become Greece's most convenient drug. There are other substances as well, of course, but in my opinion the drug of the flesh is deadlier, the more lethal transgression against God.

My confessor says so to me all the time: 'It's like you're taking drugs when you go whoring, Chrysovalantis.' He's right, for man is made in the image and likeness of God. He is a temple of the Lord. It's not on for him to destroy himself—that's suicide. And suicide is the greatest sin. Yes.

Bringing a Russian woman into your home is suicide. I know a sixty year old, a well-known gallery owner, who spends his time with a Russian woman of about twenty. What does she want with him? He might be in love, but what about her?

I am tired. Very tired. The banks and the legal threat letters are hounding me. My blood sugar sky-rockets. I don't know where I'll end up. The banking system in Greece at the moment is a bottomless pit. The bank gives you a card, a personal or a consumer loan, they plead with you to take it, and then, if you have diffi-culty paying it off, they say, 'You should have been careful,' and do their worst. They set everything in mo-tion to reclaim their money, regardless of whether it's unconstitutional or illegal. They will do anything. They destroy people.

At the bakery on Nikis Street where I get my morn-ing cheese pie, the serving girls always ask me if I've found a job. I feel awkward and change the conversa-tion. There's a sweet girl, Despina, who is particularly keen on asking me if I've found a job.

'Despina, darling', I said one day, 'if I find a job, I'll come right away and take you out.'

She turned red as a beetroot. I did it deliberately, so she wouldn't ask again.

When you have no money, no one wants to know you. Gone are the days when one woman after another would be chasing me. Now that I have no money, they say, 'Ah, he's in debt.' Unfortunately, it's worse to be in debt than to be poor. I don't know where this situation

is heading. I hope I manage with this job at the printers. I need God to step in. I'm so tired.

I see the well-dressed girls on the road with their
mobile phones and I'm puzzled. I see little squirts buying cheese pies with fifty-euro notes. Who are they
milking? Their dad? Who? (Are they university gradu-
ates already in a position?). I see the jeweller's full of
jewels, shops with clothes and shoes piled high in the
windows. Which women are buying them? Rather,
who is buying them for them? Has Greek society never
wondered?

These women are gulls. Gulls smell fish. They spy it,
dive and whisk it off. That's what they are: gulls. They
know where to find something to eat. They don't go to
the pimp, the rodent, the professional. They go to the
naïve chap. As they did to me. That's the sad conclusion.

This was my way of life until some years ago. I loved
prostitutes not as sinful women, but as creatures of
God struggling with unfavourable economic and family circumstances. You see, a woman who becomes a
prostitute has a past. She might have three or four children and a crippled, disabled father; she might have
been kicked out of her home—any number of things. I
see her as a permanently caged bird and I give her a
morsel to eat. I give her spiritual contact, courage
—and my tuppence. I won't change my mind about
prostitutes. A prostitute is one thing, a whore is quite
another. A prostitute is a woman who carries out a vo-

cation; a whore is Eumorphia, Roro and so many others. It's a long list. Yes.

I can't deny that I miss that way of life a lot, but I try —by prayer, genuflexion, vigils, etc.—not to relapse and fall back into sin. God, don't lead me into debauchery again, nor masturbation—I soil my own soul. I fall into the mire. I struggle. I think that free sex with a prostitute is a mutated form of pleasure. It's not true pleasure. I believe that now, but I didn't before, for I was always opposed to any kind of oppression and prohibition. Since I was little I preferred to play billiards or read books that my parents didn't approve of. I wanted freedom, like the ant that leaves its nest and doesn't care if the entrance gets blocked and he can never go back.

The harlot came to you, Lover of Mankind, pouring myrrh and tears over your feet. At your command she was delivered from the stench of her evil deeds, but your graceless disciple, though breathing your grace, rejected it and wallowed instead in filth, selling you in his love of money. Glory, o Christ, to your compassion.

I often go to the Neon Café on Syntagma Square, to hear the English and French of the tourists—so that if I marry an English or French woman, I will be accustomed to the sounds of her language.

I met a Russian waitress there who made eyes at me. I won't lie: I liked her, too. That's why I started frequenting the place.

One day she saw her opportunity and said, 'Can I come by for coffee at yours?'

I wanted to avoid her. 'I'm afraid not. My mother's away and it's a mess... There aren't even light bulbs in the sitting room...' (It was true, the chandelier was broken.) There was no way she could come to my house: apart from anything else, I would have a problem with my parents. (As is well known, the Greek still keeps his traditional, family mentality).

Anyway, darling, say you've got in, but why? Why should you? Did you come to play backgammon? To eat? To sleep?

I have never let females into my home.

> *I asked you baby*
> *For a drop to drink.*
> *Now give to me*
> *A kiss so lovely*
> *So I can live more deeply*
> *On life's hard journey*
> *And don't take that drop from me*
> *Even though you are me.*
>
> *I kiss you with love*
> *Like a bride gives herself up*
> *To a six-foot negro.*

I proceed to an analysis of the poem, in particular the last three lines, which are the most obscure due to their symbolism.

'I kiss you with love': that is, I kiss you with a lot of love, not the kiss of Judas but a kiss of passion. Imagine it's summer, the sun is beating down hard, you've had no water for days, and your lips are cracked—until, at last, a tender-hearted girl comes along and kisses you, and you're healed at once.

'As a bride gives herself up to a six-foot negro': Imagine there's some glam wedding, for example, between the famous singer Amanda and the equally famous basketball star C. Among the guests is a coloured chap, a friend and teammate of C. on the Italian team. At some point, the coloured Juventus player needs a piss. At the same time the bride needs the same. They go to the toilet but realise there is only one, for both men and women. The black man goes in first, but his penis is still hanging out as he leaves. The bride dashes in and bumps into the phallic black man, who leaves a great smear on her expensive wedding dress. His fluorescent fluid on her dress makes a strange polka-dot pattern in the night.

You should analyse your writing so as not to be misunderstood. The only poet not to analyse his poetry was Solomos. Seferis, Elytis and Ritsos have all done it. I analyse mine because it's a method of getting out of myself. I relax a bit and forget myself.

Russian women still carry the remains of old Sovietism—especially its insecurity. Everyone who has lived there learned to seal their lips, and they took anyone they didn't know for an informer. So, when a Russian woman comes to Greece, she wants a Greek bloke, because he doesn't have her communist mentality—he's not suspicious, he doesn't know about the KGB. She, however, knows how to cover her back and it doesn't bother her if Dimitris has five children, or if Giorgos is on the brink, or if Chrysovalantis is in debt. Then the tall tales begin, and us good and faithful Greeks gobble it all up: 'My mother is in hospital... The mafia stole my sister... My child is hungry... I have no leave to remain... The lawyer wants money...' And as soon as they've cleaned you out, they move onto the next. While you're in disrepair, they say to their friend, 'The idiot, let him suffer...'

That is the mindset of communist women: we'll all have a great time, and let the others eat cake.

I'm more restrained now since I have no money and I'm out of a job. If you have no money, you get into the rut of self-criticism. Let's remember that old painting 'The Cash-Seller and the Seller-on-Trust'. The cash-seller is doing fine, he's calm and happy, while the seller-on-trust is in dark despair, holding his head in his hands. That's what I'm like now. I'm a seller-on-trust—I entrusted myself to the banks and now I'm torn to pieces by my self-criticism. I don't think a woman can come near me now. No way. For when a woman makes a male friend, her aim is always to profit. In many ways. Particularly Russian women. Today's woman shows herself off and makes herself a shop window—she becomes a shop window to bring in cash. She becomes the so-called 'carnal slot.'

I've just remembered Megaera, another obnoxious boss. Megaera and Old Nick would make the perfect monster couple. She was also a publisher, and she exploited her father's name no end. He was a distinguished, honourable and well-educated businessman.

She put her first husband through the mill, poor thing (a lawyer), then she married again (a civil engineer) and tormented him too, and then she married a man of independent means (supposedly a sculptor) and they started a publishing house. He put up the capital and she ran the show. I don't think she was a book-lover, though. Anything but. She had no culture, as her father had. What's more, her mouth was a sewer. With me, in particular, it was open season: 'You can tell your bookbinder friend to go fuck himself!' or 'You're an imbecile, you're an idiot, I have to face it.'

She came to her father's funeral in a white suit and a black picture hat, and during the wake she was making business deals over coffee. The day after the funeral she invited me to her house to check the corrections I'd made on a book jacket. She flew at me and her mother had to step in: 'Why are you shouting at the fat young man?'

Later we heard that she and her sister had been putting small doses of arsenic in their father's tea for years, so they could inherit sooner.

She belongs to the class of crocodilian women, who cry in front of you on a whim, burden you emotionally and psychologically to do things for them, and then they pretend to have morals when really they're first-rate whores.

A week after New Year's, 1992, I think, when she had gathered us together to cut the New Year cake, she said, 'The year before last, I went without Nikos' —sideways glance at her husband—'to Denmark. The Greek ambassador confessed his love to me and proposed marriage.' She said it as if nothing had happened, completely indifferent to her husband's presence. Of course, she wanted to pull his pants down and humiliate him. When men fall into the gloved hands of unscrupulous rogues (the gloved hands of a respectable and dignified woman!), there's no escape. Woe to those who fall into such hands! For, as we all know, those hands are knives. She gave me peanuts every month (less than the basic wage of an unskilled labourer) and didn't pay my insurance—even though I brought her no end of work. I developed a whole load of solutions and patents for her, gave her contacts, and secured low prices at the printers. She didn't respect any of it. And when I put her in touch with Mr S., one of the best and most distinguished craftsmen in our field, she turned to me and said, 'He's not worthy even to kiss my feet.'

She always spoke so coarsely, like the worst whore on Athinas Street. That's why I up and left one day. Later she came looking for me. But the books she produced then were hideous and nothing like the ones that came out when I was there.

Stay away from that sort of person, those degenerates with cunning eyes and tiger faces.

I don't know why women approach me. Either they think I'm a fool or they see me as an egg they want to crack to eat the yoke. They know I'm broke. The days are gone of Eumorphia, Roro and the others spending my last pennies—Eumorphia in particular, when she saw that there was nothing left of me to take, when she had bled me white, she moved speedily onto her next victim. In any case, when I see women approaching now, I get out of the way.

A poor woman, however, puts me in a muddle. If only we were back in the good days: I would see if she was honourable, and perhaps make her my wife. But it's too late now, even for the poor ones. And Marinaki is nowhere to be seen.

Something tragic has happened to my father: he was hit by a car. I am trying to make progress with the Greek State and I cannot. I run to and fro: to the police department, the Army Pension Fund, the insurance of the driver who hit him. The situation's a mess and the answers they give me are vague and chaotic, public-servant-ish: sardonic looks which imply, 'Mate, why are you putting us to this bother? What do we care about your father's life? Won't the two of you just leave us alone?'

A truly beautiful and serious girl has a full emotional world and feels secure. She has no need to show off her thighs. None at all. For example, does the princess of Belgium need to go out topless? No, she's a princess, she has no need to deceive. While the next girl goes around with her tits out in case she can snare some rich bloke. Woman wants to take. It doesn't matter if it's five euros or a million dollars. The taking is enough. That's the mentality of the leech-woman.

When I eat I don't want anyone talking to me. I want to enjoy my food and watch the news. Eating time is sacred. Just like news-watching time.

Old Nick led me a merry dance. In time I saw that his madness and depravity were hereditary: all of his family had it.

One Saturday morning he called me to go swimming: 'My cousin Homer will take us in his car.'

As soon as we were introduced and I saw the look in his eye, the sideways twitch of his mouth and the rhythmical raising of his eyebrows, perfectly in time with the shrug of his shoulders, I suspected I'd come across another lunatic.

When we had set out, Old Nick said, 'How's things? Did you beat the wife today?'

'Of course! Every morning... I have to... so she'll learn.'

'Learn what, Homer?'

'Ancient Greek history!'

When we got to the beach he didn't even put his foot in the water, he just ran up and down.

The high point, however, came on the return. The madman turned his car into an aeroplane, since Old Nick had said he wanted to reach the supermarket before it closed. I won't number all the red lights we jumped, the pavements we mounted, the one-way streets we went down. It's a mystery how we didn't collide with even one lamp post. God kept us safe.

The next day, Old Nick said, 'Did Homer shock you yesterday? It's all par for the course. That's life: harsh and unforgiving.'

In my view, waking up, you want to wash and comb yourself (Homer was bald, of course), change your underwear, brush your teeth. But Homer, from what Old Nick said, would beat his wife, then beat her again and when he'd worked up a sweat, he would have a shower while singing the same song by Kafasis every time, his spirits soaring: 'Now you mention it, now you mention it, it's almost always the men to blame for it.'

The subject of marriage has preoccupied me since I was twenty-five years old. Sadly, if we're being honest, no woman took me seriously. I wasn't some mafioso. And for a woman to value you, you have to be a mafioso. Woman esteems man only when she fears him.

I am not interested in marriage any more. I'm sick of it. Now this one, now the next—I realised that there was no prospect. Ultimately, I don't know what women want. What do they want from a man like me? Unless they don't consider me a man. That is also a possibility. I don't want to become their plaything. Nor their pack animal—a bull dragged around by the female (I've made my mistakes and I shy away now).

I'm not sure, perhaps my appearance is to blame, or my mentality. Perhaps they all think I have a strict family and theirs won't be allowed anywhere near, or they suspect that they aren't likely to acquire any property—there's nothing to my name, after all. Perhaps, perhaps, perhaps… Who knows. In any case, marriage concerns me now only for my lack of companionship. Not the sex. No.

I wonder if the modern twenty-somethings or thirty-year-olds have been so satiated with shagging now they don't care about anything. It's a mystery. I'm of the old school—Paris of the 1910s or '20s, when a modest girl would wait in her room until her parents went to sleep, and then beautiful minstrels would pass under her balcony serenading her with romantic songs.

In the modern age, unfortunately, the characteristics of the Greek woman—as well as of the new immigrants—are: phone, fancy car, avarice. That's why it's no problem for them to sleep with a seventy- or eighty-year-old fellow. As long as they get his signature… All of them stake their bets on the inheritance. I know a seventy-five-year-old general who married a Ukrainian woman of twenty-two. The moment she got his signature, that was it. The general himself told me, 'One day she went shopping and she still hasn't come back…'

By the end, Old Nick had overloaded us with work and there was no messing around. He deliberately started acting erratically, to exhaust us. He himself had gone under completely. He wanted to get rid of us painlessly—for us to quit without making demands. That was his goal, and that's why he had it on his agenda to swear at at least three of his fifty-five employees every day.

A respectable senior priest that I spoke to during confession said, 'He's capricious and doesn't know what he wants. Beware!'

One day when I was on the third floor with the graphic artists, Old Nick flew at M. Since the offices are only separated by Plexiglas, everyone could hear.

'You still haven't prepared the mock-ups?! I'm at the end of my tether! What's going on? Who's in charge here?' He was foaming at the mouth.

As soon as he saw her cry, he burst into T.'s office, screaming.

'Where are the invoices? Are you trying to annoy me?'

When T. threw the invoices down, shouting, 'Take them, they're ready!' and left the office in a huff, Old Nick's bubble burst, he was embarrassed and came next into my office. He sat opposite me, breathing heavily.

'Could you make me some tea?'

When I brought it to him, he said, 'You know what happens? Sometimes I have the idea that none of you are really you, but others who look like you—that's why I have to check that you love me... You can't imagine how sorry I am when I verify that you are real, and that I've hurt you...'

He was confused. And it was his schizophrenia that was running this test. To prove that it really was me, I sat there and listened silently.

In truth, he hadn't always been so paranoid. When I met him he was an honest businessman. He was the general secretary of the Association of Lithographers. Everyone introduced him to me as generous and prompt with payment. Indeed, he paid me much more than I was expecting. My first salary was a hundred and twenty thousand. And he was always polite and sweet with all of us. Later things went awry and his madness kicked in.

You'll say that women also are sweet when they first get into a relationship. But if the boat starts to capsize, they leave all of a sudden, and all their sweetness, affection and kisses were for nothing. That's what it's like, unfortunately. And the days I wasted with Old Nick cannot be reclaimed.

I can imagine myself as a monk, but I don't know if I could take it. It would be a great test of my soul. You have to abandon worldly things, ambition, career, marriage, dreams. Chuck in your former life and start a new one. Now, you'll say, what do you prefer, a psychiatrist or the Holy Mountain? The big problem is if one wants to follow a monastic life voluntarily. Say he's fed up with women and generally with life, and sees monastic life as a means of escape, an ultimate solution: that's a huge mistake, and a sin. I am a good pilgrim, so God accepts me, whereas He might cast me out if I don the habit. He doesn't want hypocrites. 'The Lord will abhor the bloody and deceitful man.'

He wants me as a pilgrim, for He knows that I'll go out and do things, that I will live a more moral life on Earth. I will find peace. That's why He accepts it—otherwise He would not. It wouldn't be right for me to go to the Holy Mountain and be thinking about a Russian woman's thighs.

Life goes on. And life is tough.

If it's possible, in a year I would like to have married and knocked her up, so that I can become a father soon enough. I want to give myself some dignity and

I believe that the vagina could offer that. I hope I'm not wrong. I also want a house of my own to live in with my wife and child. (It wouldn't be right to live with my parents and sisters.) A small, modest house, somewhere on the coast between Athens and Corinth—or a little flat, let's say fifty square metres, in London.

Within those few square metres I want to build our life, our love, our dreams. If I find out that while I'm out at work she has played the field, there are two options: either I run off to a monastery, or I go straight to a psychiatrist. And then perhaps I would make her repent for her sinful ways. With my dignified stance, I would make her feel very guilty indeed.

> *My whole life is a lady—*
> *One moment she's so warm and lovely*
> *The next she throws me in the freezer.*

If a woman falls into the sin of adultery, it means she has passed beyond all contrition and become corrupted. The man gets pleasure from adultery, but the woman gets the banner of corruption. I would go to the psychiatrist for revenge, so that everyone would say, 'Shame on you, you debased woman, you've driven the bloke mad!' On the other hand, I would go to a monastery more for my own personal peace, to forget her. I believe that when you sit down and tell an old man in a tattered habit about your pain, then God grants peace to your soul.

On the subject of age, I don't mind breaking a taboo: I want my wife to be at least ten or fifteen years younger than me. A greater difference wouldn't bother me either, even if everyone says, 'There's grandpa with his bit of skirt.' If you're asking, Marinaki was a nice bit of skirt—practically a model. Roro wasn't so beautiful, but certainly screwable. Her womanhood screamed at you from a mile off. She sent off signals. I'm not saying that anyone who dresses like that is a whore, and the others are good. Allow me to explain: even Megaera, although she wore conservative suits, was at heart a whore. Old Nick's wife also dressed modestly, but she had snakes in her heart. I don't judge the clothing, therefore, but what's inside.

My friend X. told me that he saw Roro with her new bloke. He's so charmless, apparently, that X. can't understand why she has anything to do with him. Six-foot tall and skinny as a telegraph pole. I think, therefore, that most women are rotten inside. Does she really think that graceless beanpole is the real deal?

I think I might give my autobiography the title, 'Memories of a Tasteless Life.' You see, I started off differently—I believed in grand ideas and people, and I ended up a sick beggar.

I read in the classified ads that they were looking for a new television presenter. I called and found out which channel it was. Second-rate, to be honest, but it would do. I went to their offices, completed the application, and the secretary said, 'Come to the studio tomorrow morning for an audition.'

I went the next day in my suit, cologne, etc. There were eighty of us—men and women—waiting in line. After about four hours they called me in. I stood in front of the camera. I had butterflies at first, naturally, but I overcame them quickly because I knew I was made for the job. I read the text comfortably and seriously, and when I had finished, I heard on the loudspeaker, 'Thank you very much, we will call you in a few days.' They never called me, of course, and I wasted one day of my life.

'It's all word of mouth with those jobs', a friend told me in the café. How was I to know?

I put sugar in my coffee to sweeten the bitter memories I have of Eumorphia. That girl, I can tell you, never even gave me a glass of water. Never.

The only plus I can find regarding Old Nick is that he brought out an energy in me which had been bolted a thousand times over inside a cupboard. Old Nick, known to everyone for his double-crossing, managed to open that cupboard and my whole lifeblood poured out, which he used exclusively for his own purposes. Of course, I gave unconditionally of myself. Unfortunately.

Yesterday I went for coffee with a good friend and we had a serious discussion about my future. As we were talking, he received a phone call and needed to speak for a long time. Before he finished, I knocked up a little poem and dedicated it to him. I wrote it because when I feel anguish and sorrow, poetry always functions as consolation.

> *I gaze at you, I gaze at you*
> *For your company I long*
> *With a will that's strong*
> *And friendship true.*
> *I tell this to you right out—*
> *Me, cunning as a fox*
> *And clever as a cat.*

'Your friend Chrysovalantis has changed,' I said to him when he read it. 'He has turned over a new leaf. He's no longer the middle-aged, half-employed lithographer, Old-Nick's-dogsbody that you knew. Chrysovalantis is now a virgin-born soul.'

'Mate, I wish you the best,' he responded and put the poem in the inside pocket of his jacket. That moved me a lot.

I had a dream. I speculate that we were somewhere in Megalo Pefko. My father and I. We had just come back from hospital. 'Come on,' he said, 'I'm going to take you somewhere.' We got into a little boat—we only just fit, mainly due to my taking up all the space. In one hand he held his little urine bag and with the other he rowed. We reached a house in the sea and he said, 'We're here.' I was perturbed to find that it was Eumorphia's family home. The door suddenly opened. We went in and saw seven boats, one next to the other, and seven Eumorphias sleeping in them. I stared goggle-eyed and said, 'What the hell am I doing in this hole?' I grabbed the oars in terror and began to row like a madman. Then we were on a green tractor. Before I turned it on, however, I realised that I had left Father's health insurance booklet in Eumorphia's house. I went and retrieved it (the seven monsters were still asleep) and returned. Arriving back home, I realised that I was driving a red tractor and that I had left Father on the green one.

When I woke up I was wracked with guilt. My father shouldn't pay for the nasty, damaging company I keep. If I go under, nothing would induce me to want him to fall into the hands of such rodent-women.

On the other hand, it's possible that the seven rodents were in fact my seven bosses. In total, they robbed me of four million drachmas. I suppose that this dream ultimately means that I haven't achieved anything in my life that I, or my father, had wanted—to become a naval officer with a nice house in Piraeus, playing songs by Tsitsanis on a little bouzouki to warm the hearts of those in the Officers' Mess. I mean, I'd be an officer and musician. I managed neither of the two.

OK, you'll ask which of my dreams I did achieve. Well, none. Unfortunately.

I didn't even achieve the most basic one: to marry a sweet, good-natured, nymph-like girl with firm bosoms, good manners and good upbringing—and who never farts, of course. I would look at her every evening, swimming far out to bring back mussels for her beloved—me. She would dive in her white nightdress, not naked. It's well known that mermaids have scales to guard their genitals.

You find the most expensive rents in England and France. When I went to London with Eumorphia, I exhausted myself looking for a two-bed at a reasonable price. And then I paid a deposit five times the rent. I'd taken leave of my senses. Just as she bled me white over that time, she did the same to F. And when she returned from London with her Master's, she left him, too, in a month. She'd already found a replacement: a Cypriot estate agent. I found that out later, of course, and I still can't bear it. That's why I believe (I'm no prophet!) that when F. gets old, if he still hasn't married either, he'll commit a crime. He'll kill her.

Old Nick used to receive calls from his nephew, Z. (right now he's being treated in the Dafni Mental Hospital), at three in the morning. He would say, 'This is Charon and I'm coming to get you. Be prepared,' or,

'Put seven hundred thousand drachmas in my account and I'll save you.' Old Nick would reply, 'I have no money. I'm in financial difficulties,' in response to which Z. would ask, 'Then how does your wife buy five hundred pairs of shoes every year?'

Old Nick would call me at home immediately to tell me what happened (he said I calmed him down, since I always listened carefully and never interrupted him) and wake us all up at the crack of dawn. If I picked it up, I would hear his voice and doze off, but if my father got there first, he would give him what for.

'Excuse me, do you think we're as full of beans as you?'

When I was eighteen, a friend sent me to a whorehouse in Kolonaki, on the corner of Loukianou Street and Alopekis Street. It was an elegant half-basement copulation zone. That's where I met Sonia. She was a beautiful blonde (I venture that it was natural) who never let me down. I always wanted the woman I saw to treat me tenderly in bed. I would look at her hands first to see if she was a junkie, and then I would bend an ear to see how she spoke to the madam. If I heard her swear, I would get up and go. I wanted the woman I would sleep with to be tender and kind to everyone. I expected to reach an intellectual orgasm. I would observe myself: after a quarter of an hour, will I have the same desire as I had when I set out from Korydallos? If the desire wanes, it's useless, the erection goes flat and my emotional state does the same. Sex, after all, has an emotional aspect.

> I asked him again, saying, 'Sir, since once thou dost bear with me, declare unto me this further matter also.' 'Say on,' saith he. 'If a wife, Sir,' say I, 'or, it may be, a husband fall asleep, and one of them marry, doth the one that marrieth sin?' 'He sinneth not,' saith he, 'but if he remain single, he investeth himself with more exceeding honour and with great glory before the Lord; yet even if he should marry, he sinneth not.'

I'm struggling to remain where I am and not sink any lower.

From time to time, various women approach me and I wonder if they are temptations of the Devil. What, after all, do they expect from a person in dire straits? A woman spots right away if a man is a success or failure. She can even spot it from the telephone directory, if she sees 'businessman', 'lawyer', 'architect' or 'surgeon, graduate of such-and-such' next to his name. If she sees that next to Chrysovalantis's name there is absolutely nothing, not even 'lithographer', she twigs that the person is a good-for-nothing.

Mr S., a professor at Athens University, once said to me, 'In my village there's a saying that if a bucket has a hole in it and you lower it into the well, it won't gather water, but it will get damp.' That's just like me. I go to the monasteries of the Holy Mountain, with all the monks who care for me and love me, because I believe that I'm a bucket without a bottom—but at least if I fall into the saintly well, a few drops will stick to me.

My future is in sales, not in production. I can't put up with the manual labour of the lithographer anymore. I prefer to visit small publishers and make advantageous counterproposals for their book production. I want to become a respectable middle-man. I have experience in our field. Books interest me greatly. Let's make this happen.

I've had funny cases of women, but the ones that have hurt me the most were Roro and Eumorphia. Eumorphia in particular—I am amazed that at her wedding three years ago, all those she had deceived didn't come and protest outside the church.

With Eumorphia I felt that the female Judas had killed me. Yes. Christ was merely betrayed by Judas, but this one betrayed *and* killed me. I'm still not over it. Not that I'm in love with her, but I still cannot forgive myself for becoming such a victim.

I try with prayer, with vigil. I go to the Petraki Monastery and say, 'God, please save me. Find me a girl to marry.' My patron saints are the Holy Virgin, St Anna and St Anthony.

God says, 'Wait,' then 'No,' then 'Yes—here and now, lose weight; lower your blood sugar; fix your teeth.' Once He said to me, 'You have a beautiful face, you're

a cultivated individual, but your umbrella is broken.'
Yes. I know that too.

If a woman sees me like this, she'd be embarrassed
to go around with me. There was a short time, however, when I did freestyle wrestling. Now I've really let
myself go. When I worked out, I was alright, but when
I abandoned it, due (mainly) to my workload, I began
to lard up. I liked being athletic, it was a kind of discipline: coming and going as I pleased, doing all the ex-
ercises I needed to, training with athletes that I
admired. And, of course, the fact that I could make
friends there. I love making new friends.

On the Holy Mountain they told me that it's not
good to approach all and sundry, but I know that Christ
even approached the scribes and Pharisees and simple
people. I, too, decided to love everyone. That was rather
my undoing, however, as my life became a thorough-
fare. I threw myself away. I have given so much and I
don't know if I will ever harvest the vine I pruned, dug,
watered and cared for all these years. Women have
never shown understanding to me. I found more in
prostitutes than in ladies. The highfalutin women who
have three kinds of lipstick in their handbag and three
mobile phones don't care about anyone; they're just
good-time girls. Where to begin with them? And where
to end? They're all ultimately the same.

I have taken my apprenticeship and earned my medal
—I have worn the devilish cloak of Old Nick right

against my skin. When an athlete runs once, twice, three times, ten times around the track, at some point he will win a medal. I ran around Old Nick's track, but the only medal I won was a slap in the face.

I systematically investigate the face of every woman. Is it troubled? Is it smiley? Is it well-looked-after? Is there a touch of excitement or perhaps a whimsical sadness? Has she finally thrown off the reins? If you see her eyebrows plucked, you know she's going to pluck your eyes out. Guaranteed. I recognise now if a woman wants me for my money—if she really fancies me or if she's taking me for a ride. I just know. I've been there.

I would like to marry a divorcee. I would prefer her to have children so she wouldn't ask me for any—I don't think I could do it.

I would like to hear those little voices saying, 'Daddy, Daddy.' I want to marry an English girl. I know she wouldn't cheat, regardless of my performance. An English woman keeps a good home, the whole run of the house is under her command, and she doesn't want to go out to work. Nor would I want her to work— imagine all the people she would meet in the office! Someone's bound to make a pass.

Yes. Better an English woman, who wouldn't mind living with her in-laws. The Swedes are similarly ac-commodating. Don't fear fresh-faced people. Don't fear the criminal who has come out of prison after forty years. He won't reoffend. He has repented.

Do fear the Chinese. The Chinese chap says one thing and does another. The same with the Japanese. That's why America is afraid of them and since the Second World War hasn't gone near them. Better an ally and friend at a distance than an enemy, they say. The mind of the Japanese is fifty times faster on technological issues than that of the American. If you give him a computer programme, he will learn it in a day, whereas the American would need ten. If you give the Japanese something to assemble, he will do it in the blink of an eye and without a second thought, whereas the American needs a plan and detailed instructions. Now, if you give a Russian something to assemble for you, he'll say, 'Why are you tormenting me?' Give him vodka and he's happy. I've worked with Russians. I know.

The work sector concerns me a great deal. At the moment our field is susceptible. People don't care about good books or journals. Other things are being sold in our times, unfortunately.

I had a very bad experience recently with someone who offered me work but wanted to bring me down. 'I still haven't understood what you know about our field,' he said. When I heard this, I walked out.

Technology has hit me three times: firstly in typesetting, then in filmsetting and finally with montage. All three were abandoned. Now I'm stuck in the field of quality control and costing. I want to get into sales as well. I think it's a field with prospects, even though I see many good salespeople from our sector going into mobile phone and clothes sales, since it's more prosperous and you get higher percentages. A publisher cannot give huge percentages to the salesperson, the way—for example—multinationals can. The book business is not for getting rich. It's not a goldmine or a shipping firm. In the book world you give ten and receive one in return. You'll ask me why I persist in this field. Because it suffices for me. Nor do I mean to lay down my weapons at the age of fifty—for I believe that if we, the old guard, leave, then the book might fall into dangerous hands. And also because I don't know what else I would do.

A book is like a knife:
A housewife picks it up and cuts bread,
A butcher picks it up and cuts meat,
The murderer picks it up and takes a life.

Now I think that for my autobiography a more fitting title would be 'A Barefaced Life'. If they read what happened with Madame Eumorphia, they'll shake their heads. They'll say, 'You gave her so much, you spent so much on her, she ran you around, and you didn't manage to get her into bed even once?' Yes. My readers may be right, but I didn't want to pressure her. That's not in my character. Plus, of course, I believe in the Holy Scriptures. On the other hand, to tell the harsh truth:

I don't consider sex a primary necessity. It's not like going to the toilet. That's why God gave us masturbation, so we wouldn't fall into the great sins of prostitution and rape. Bestiality is also a great sin. They say that the Australians copulate with kangaroos and ostriches and it's considered a criminal offence. When man abandons reading, music and pure friendship, he strays down deviant and completely unnatural paths. Yes.

I have suffered at the hands of builders, bosses and one or two priests. I still remember the beating I took from a head priest, the director of the Church printers, when once I disobeyed and left work to go for a walk on Lykavettos hill. When I returned, I got the talking-to of the year. I was thirteen or fourteen. Priests (I want to stress this) are the harshest employers. Along with former communists and the nouveaux riches. The worst.

I was a ship with many ropes, and the towboats were pulling me back and forth. When I came back from work, my parents shouted at me, 'What time do you call this? What about school? You'll rack up too many absences.' At work they forced me to do overtime, saying, 'What do you want to go to school for? You'll learn your craft here.'

It's not in my nature to let anyone down. I wanted to please everyone. And look where I've ended up.

My diabetes was diagnosed in '93. At the hospital, however, they stressed to me that I had had it much longer. It has triggered in me a sense of relaxation, while in others it strains the nerves. I measure my blood sugar every day—morning and evening—so that the doctors can determine my progress. I also take pills and watch my diet. I shouldn't eat anything sugary or starchy. Nor must I get sad or fall in love, for they say that anxiety does no good to a diabetic. It is not recommended for diabetics to spend time with women. You might accidentally eat too much when you're with a woman, and since a diabetic is rather stubborn, when a woman lets him down, his resolve is thwarted and he turns to food: it's an easy solution. He thinks he will let off steam. Food is a refuge. But it's a labyrinth—you can't get out. Yes, I've sunk to those depths. I'm trying to get out, of course. The doctors say, 'Stay away from excesses, Chrysovalantis, stay away!' Unfortunately, women like spending time with diabetics, to wind them up. That's happened both to me and to acquaintances with the same condition. The diabetic must have faith in himself, not in others. A woman used to say to me, 'I'll heal you with my love,' but in reality, she just wanted me to take her to the best restaurants. She would eat a bellyful and say to me, 'Chrysovalantis, you mustn't eat moussaka, you mustn't eat fried things, nor pasta. Promise me you won't eat sweet things again.' And the tart was as thin as a rake. My mouth would start watering and as soon as I returned home I would raid the fridge. I had money in those days.

Put simply, she squandered my cash. I had realised this, of course, but I didn't say anything, as I wanted to have a good time. If you don't have friends to socialise with, then you pay. That's a law of nature. When you're not a natural magnet, you become a money-eating magnet and you pay. For there to be magnetism in a relationship there must also be money. It's no good without. Unfortunately. That's the case ninety-nine percent of the time.

Anyway, fruit juice, genetically modified sweets, sandwiches and soft drinks can be deadly to diabetics. You need simple food in small quantities, at least five or six times per day—dry toast, cheese, lots of water and a raisin bun instead of sweets. That's hugely frustrating. I get drowsy and have fluctuations of emotion. I get tired of moving, even though I was always overactive (if somewhat portly). Coffee is also bad for me. If I drink some in the evening and then wake up in the middle of the night, I won't be able to sleep again. No.

Over the last three years, diabetes has humiliated me. My legs hurt, I cannot stand up straight, my eyes cloud over and the drugs give me constipation. Another huge health problem has also arisen: I can't get an erection. This is very serious. I'm attracted to females, yes, I feel great desire, but… the diabetes wreaks havoc everywhere. If I become ill and take antibiotics, it's as though I haven't taken anything— the antibiotics are neutralised immediately. My heart has also been affected, the doctors said, and they still don't know what complications will arise if the illness worsens. Like a crafty suitor, diabetes has been besieging my heart for so many years.

Once a month I go to the Tzaneio Hospital to see what effect it has had on my whole body—on my nerves and muscles. I have a team of doctor friends there who look after me. They are wonderful people and scientists. I lend a hand in the publication of their books and visiting cards and they don't charge me.

Incidentally, I'm starting to go slightly lame in the left foot. I'm always getting blood clots. We don't know where the diabetes will strike in five years' time. It struck a friend of mine, forty-one years old, in the heart. He had a double bypass, poor chap.

I'm worried. Very worried. Those looking after me are worried, too. And I'm worried for them. When a doctor says to me, 'Look out, you'll have heart trouble,' while smoking a cigar, what can I reply? It's mad, it's grotesque, to try to protect your patient's health from whatever, while you are leaving your guard wide open.

The only good thing that unemployment has done for me is that I don't have money to throw at sweets and fizzy drinks. That's an austerity measure, too. So, every cloud... Oh well, that's life.

I would like my older sister to marry—to find some teacher-colleague of hers to give her a good life with a couple of children. She would make a good mother.

Strict but good. And she would make a good spouse. She knows how to look after the people she loves.

I think that it's time to publish the book I have been preparing for years. I have a hell of a lot of poems, I need to make a rigorous selection and keep only a hundred or a hundred and ten. I will let my older sister do the editing. I trust her.

There is an issue, however, about what kind of poems to put in—existential ones? satirical ones? love poems? My friend N., who has read most of them, told me that my love poems are the strongest. If in the end I only put those in, then I will give it the title, 'Roro of Love' (in homage to my mentor, that ladies' man Odysseus Elytis), with the dedication:

> *To my friend Demosthenes Zita*
> *Who never enjoyed the dolce vita.*

My new confessor is better than the old one. Well, more flexible. I believe—and I say this with great joy—that I have found the right representative of God. He says, 'Beware of women, beware!'

My old one had the same advice, but the new one says it in a better way. He's closer to my character. More compliant. He deems it right to show me every forbearance. For there are some illnesses of the soul that cannot be treated from one day to the next. Very often spiritual illnesses turn out as serious as bodily ones.

'Please don't eat too much, it'll do you no good,' he always says.

I had a crisis once, and consumed a whole tray of baklava and a kilo of kaymaki ice cream in one sitting. I told him so at confession.

He reacted vehemently: 'Why don't you listen? Diet is a matter of obedience. Be obedient!' I was shaken and wracked with guilt, but then I said, 'OK, Father, may your will be done.'

I don't want a tyrant for a confessor. I want to feel the same ease and security with him as when I go to my psychiatrist friend. My confessor is also a doctor, but of the spirit and soul, not the body. I want my confessor beside me.

Heal the wounds of my heart left by many sins. O physician of souls and bodies, grant forgiveness of faults to those who ask. Ever give me tears of penitence, releasing me from what I owe you, O Lord, and have mercy on me.

Eumorphia Circeoglou was a striking lady who would wiggle her rear-end for cash. For obvious reasons, I am using a pseudonym: Eumorphia for the ironic euphemism,[1] and Circeoglou from the evil witch Circe of the *Odyssey*. That's what she was, after all. She had any

---

[1] 'Eumorphia' in Greek means 'Well-shaped'.

number of blokes on the go, as I was informed after the show was over. She changed them like she changed shirts—now F., now the chap from Larisa, and a dozen dogsbodies who ran around after her. One such dogsbody was me. A grave error, I realise. I was deceived.

At the beginning I thought she was an angel. I was drawn by the fact that many of her girlfriends shielded her. I wanted to penetrate that shield. Her friends always surrounded her. They never left her alone. They always took her in their car. Their goal, as she herself revealed to me later, was to keep me away from her. But it charmed me. I liked the delay and the chase before the ultimate surrender. Deep down I knew there was no chance of that. And yet, I kept up the vain hope—spiritual patent medicine…

I believed that something might happen between us. After the London trip, though, I saw her true colours and cut it off. I imagined her as a nymph and thought that if we were seen hand in hand, people would say, 'That good-for-nothing has landed himself a beauty!' She wasn't exactly exciting, but she was coquettish. She liked to cause a stir. I thought we would marry, I would become a shopkeeper, a bookseller—I had money then—and she would practise graphic design at home. Lovely, peaceful and familial. Romantic. How wrong I was. Yes.

With Roro Kapernarou, however—a pseudonym again, without any particular significance—I wanted to live from the waist down. No marriage. I just wanted our juices to unite. A passionate embrace with all the trimmings. When I first saw her, I said to myself, 'I want to make her mine.' I knew that for such a woman there is no hesitation, no separation, no borders, just deep union. Her long hair and her eyes drew me in. The eyes of a cat. A stupid cat. I wanted to show her that I loved her. That's why I granted her every whim: I bought her a double bed, a leather coat, trousers and underwear, the latest mobile phone, and gave her pocket money.

The deception went on for about a year and a half. I used to go to Sparta every weekend. I would take her out for coffee, then a meal, dessert, coffee again and a drink in the evening. She would walk me to the high street, stop at the shop windows and say, 'Ah, look at that lovely underwear, those suspenders, those skirts!' 'Another time,' I would say and bought her all of it piece by piece—for as long as my finances could manage.

One day she said, 'I've lost my phone.' I bought her the latest model and put it in my name so that the bills would come to me. She had promised not to overuse it, so I wouldn't be charged too much. After about a month I called her and a man picked up—probably her bloke. 'Pronto!' he said, and I was so shaken I responded, 'Pronto what, you bastard!' and hung up.

The next day I called her.

'Was it you that called Tasos a bastard?'

'Yes.'

She hung up without another word.

Then she changed her number. Tasos was a construction worker and—as I found out later—a wife-beater. Women of her type submit easily to rogues and they ignore the good, honest young men. As the great Stelios Kazantzidis says in his philosophical song,

> *Since ladies in this world are so few*
> *Why are we such sentimentalists?*

Conclusion: Sensitive and worthy people always fall foul of heartless, female piranhas.

Today is a big day for me. I've been hired. I feel like an angel who has just grown wings. My star, dim for so long and hidden behind thick clouds, has shone today. An employer has looked on me with confidence. I am grateful to him for that.

When I went into the offices, Mr K. said, 'Go up to accounts so they can sign you on.' That brought me unimaginable joy and gave me the will to look for my first client goals at once. It's an important festival today—St Anne's day. I received a blessing from my confessor in the early morning. As if he knew, he said, 'Good luck in your new job.' And, as always, I received a tie as a present from Aunt Dionysia.

Roro, I think now, was unscrupulous—I'll say it plain. Once when I went to Sparta, her sister suggested that I stay at their house. There was nothing I wanted more, and I didn't care if my parents went looking for me.

'I'm going out for a bit and I'll be back in half an hour,' Roro said after lunch. She didn't reappear all evening. And I stayed awake waiting for her. She came back at dawn. That's when I realised how unscrupulous she was. What was she doing out until dawn? She was a liar, too—she told me she worked as a tutor and gave private lessons. What lessons? She couldn't even speak correct Greek.

My romance with Marinaki didn't find fertile ground. I loved her. I don't know if it was mutual. Luckless Marinaki. Luckless. She caught me when I had no money. We had some great conversations, though. I told her about myself, and she told me about herself. We did nothing sexually. There was always, however, an ardent, unquenchable desire. I felt it in the way she smiled at me. It glowed like an invitation in her eyes and lips, but I couldn't stick it out—my finances and diabetes were to blame. Yes.

What I will never forget is how once, on my birthday, she brought me a rose and said, 'Happy Birthday!' I looked at her and almost burst into tears.

My new job is going well. I think that this graphic design company is the best I have ever found. It's closer to home, and they promised to pay my travel. At last it seems as though things are settling down and, to tell the truth, I don't want to fall back into my old, sinful ways. I want a quiet, honourable and monkish life. Above all, to care for my family, which needs me so much now.

My boss put me in the big office because I brought him two good clients. When he was informed that some folk were trying to sabotage me, he came and asked, 'How are you getting on with the others?'

'Very well!' I said. What could I say? I'm interested in the good of the company. Keeping a balance is everything.

At home I'm a monk. Literally. It's not that I go wild when I'm out, but I do believe that at the age I've reached, I need to be a proper man. It's difficult now, I know. Let's be real. I prefer, as the proverb says, 'a shoe from your own country, even if it's patchy,' to those flighty things who God knows what kind of life they led in Russia, or wherever. Then again, girls from Patras are no better.

Could I forget that other one, who worked on the ships, on the Patras-Ancona line? There were so many jobs, why did she choose the ships, just to be swayed back and forth by the sea? I think she went in for orgies. Her mind was rotten. Corrupt. For women, orgies are worse than prostitution—they're a departure from natural sex. Sexual deviancy has many stages. They even say that anal sex is deviant, just like homosexuality and bestiality. Many people fornicate with rabbits. Who knows? I've worked since I was young—since I was twelve years old. I did so to learn my craft—the craft of typography. I learned it first hand, since my old confessor, Father T., was the head of the Church printers. I first went there with my parents, and when I saw the machines, the ink and the paper, I was enchanted. After that I went every day after school. I realised that I didn't like studying much and I thought I would devote myself professionally to typography.

I finished secondary school and before my military service, a friend of my father bent over backwards to get me into the Permanent Commissioned Officers School. Yes, they pressured me. I went to the school in Trikala. I soon realised, however, that I don't like the army. That horrendous discipline. And the hypocrisy. 'Don't swear, don't smoke, don't eat like that, shave, button yourself up,' etc. They thought they were talking to some illiterate ignoramus. They thought I couldn't see their debauchery. Me, who had lived beside people of civilisation and spirituality my whole life. Then any old ranker would come along, some upstart from the Army Academy, and knock me down.

We once had an inspection in the barracks from Second Lieutenant G.M. Apparently, I hadn't organised the clothes locker, and when he saw it he started to kick it furiously right before my eyes. I went to the commanding officer in tears. 'I want to leave the school.'

'Why? Did he hurt the locker?' he sneered, and then he ordered me to go back and didn't do anything to that bastard of a second lieutenant.

They told me to toughen up and leave my sensitivities to one side, because when I become a sergeant, I would need to be strong and unyielding to confront the drug-addict, thief, criminal and enemy of the country. I didn't believe that, however, nor do I believe it now. If people behaved like that, we would have five hundred murders every day.

I am in favour of diplomacy. We can find a number of ways to bring equilibrium to the social and political system. When a doctor wants to tranquilise a psychopath, he doesn't put him in handcuffs, he slips a pill secretly into his orange juice and says, 'Come on, sit down and have a drink.' He doesn't exert force. He doesn't try to hang him.

Unfortunately the Greek Army is behind in this. Far behind. Violent behaviour towards sensitive individuals is the norm. Officers forget their inhibitions. I mean, if an officer's wife doesn't do her duty to him one night, he will take it out on the poor lads. The lads on military service, unfortunately, pay for the poor marital and sexual life of the officers. It was that kind of lieutenant who said to me one day, 'Now that it's cold, little Chrysovalantis, and there's a metre of snow, I'll send you onto the balcony of the company administration to play with your little prick.' He said it in front of everyone to ridicule me and break my spirit. There's a whole load of other things which I don't want to remember. (In any case, it's still a mystery—I am fifty and I can't explain it: to what purpose was all this cruelty towards my person? Why? I still carry this resentment inside me!)

I quit the school, of course, to my father's great displeasure.

I come now to the case of a homosexual and a woman from Patras. The three of us worked together for Old Nick: Z., L., and yours truly. Z. was a little queer. Let me be honest: I hadn't actually seen him do anything, but some colleagues assured me that he batted for the other team. I don't want to slander him—I repeat, I never saw anything myself—but others said so. Both of them were Old Nick's secretaries. L. fussed about the pizza order from morning to lunchtime—she had the leaflet in front of her and would read it again and again. While the other chap was glued to television magazines. Since Old Nick overloaded them (as he did all of us), they would explode at each other with no reason and not do their work. They would argue with each other about the smallest things and then have it out with their friends on the telephone. Not with lovers but with friends—I don't think either of them had a relationship. I could see it in their eyes. Along with the frustration they underwent on a daily basis, this led both of them, I conjecture, to masturbate every night.

In the case of Z., the homosexual, I cannot express an opinion on how he carried out his self-gratification. I have never heard or read the relevant material. The fact that he is a puffter does not concern me. It's his right. He will answer to God on the matter.

As regards L. (I know that many other spinsters do this, too, since they really take their rejection to heart), I imagine her drinking whiskies and then falling into bed to satisfy herself. But if this becomes a habit, it creates an inflammation in the soul. I know that. It's a fact.

I want to speak about the mentality of women, from their waking up in the morning to the evening when they complete their daily routine. I intend to dig a little deeper, right into their inner selves: how they operate from the moment they go home and undress to the moment they fall asleep. It is a very serious subject and has concerned me repeatedly, that's why I sought the assistance of a psychiatrist I know, who is a military doctor and director of a large hospital. Mr Anagnostou gave me various pieces of information to make a detailed analysis on the subject. (I might publish it someday. We'll see.)

The mind of woman is in a constant state of over-excitation, to ensure her the means to live happily, comfortably and parasitically. For example, she doesn't forget what she needs to eat to maintain her figure. Will she eat non-fattening salad? Or will she eat fatty nuts? Will she eat meat that has little fat but does have calories? Or will she eat a man? She has thought of everything, it's all in that mixing pot. That's why a woman cannot be productive at work—a million issues are bothering her, and she wants to solve them all at once. My little sister told me about a nurse who left her shift to do some shopping. She vanished and everyone went looking for her.

A man cannot get up to such tricks so openly. Not that there aren't cases like that, of course—such as the sick man who wants to go to the races to bet on Astrakhan or Wagtail and says to his boss, 'My grandma has died, I need a deposit for the funeral.' He comes back a couple of days later without a penny to his name.

With men, this happens once every so often. With the great majority of women, it's the norm. For they know that since men are kindly disposed to the female gender, they make professional allowances for them. In this way, a woman easily deceives a man and does what she wants. She relishes taking her bloke for a ride—or her son, colleague or boss. That's the so-called 'women's disorder'. Tatiana did this when she said to her partner, 'Go to three betting shops and put something down on the match. Good luck.' He did her the favour because he thought she was superstitious. But she did it to sneak as many kisses as she could from me.

Question one: Is man in a position to support the male gender against cunning females? Question two: What is the world coming to?

I think that if I lose some weight I will be handsome. I need to do so anyway because my health is in danger. My sisters tell me that all the time. I look at myself in the mirror and I despair. My veins are swollen and my rolls are bulging. The way I'm heading, at some point my diabetes will destroy me. That's also what my doctors at the Tzaneio said. I need to lose at least thirty-five kilos, which as I get older becomes more and more difficult. The last two years I made a concerted effort and lost about seven—I was a hundred and thirty-eight and now I am a hundred and thirty-one. But I need to lose more. I'm one metre seventy; I'm no giant. I have no psychological support, however, nor stimulus: like a romance, for example.

'Eat wholegrain breads and vegetable products,' Old Nick once said to me. I believed him and I put on six kilos…

Yes, I need to lose weight. I need to give myself one final chance before I am led to self-destruction. It's not easy to lose so much, now I mention it, but hope dies last.

I was OK until '85. I didn't exceed ninety-three kilos. I worked hard. I ran between typographers and publishers, and on the weekends I worked surveillance for a detective. I stopped because the poor chap was killed. We never found out why or by whom.

Then, perhaps from my sadness, or perhaps my exhaustion and lack of a suitable woman, I turned to food. I bought a sandwich at every corner shop, cheese pies, sweets, soft drinks. I have repented for all of this—if only I could begin a new life, but my diabetes doesn't allow it. You don't climb up life with an escalator. When you go up the stairs alone, life brings you ten stairs back, and you find yourself where you started or even further back. The years fly by and never return.

In the workplace there were some people who couldn't stand me, such as Mopface. She couldn't stand me at all, for I had never looked at her sexually. That got on her nerves. She was ugly and unloved. She was jealous that I liked her friend Eumorphia so much more. When I stared at Eumorphia, I really got my fill: my glances were forks with which I devoured her (then) sweet beauty, forkfuls of her golden pasta—her blonde hair. All that irritated Mopface, and that's why she ganged up with A. and didn't let me near Eumorphia. 'For a woman to look at you,' Mopface told me, 'you need to be handsome. Go to a slimming club.' I didn't reply, but I became even more emotionally burdened and went for her friend as much as I could, until I became tiresome. Since Eumorphia liked compliments (like a vicious, barking dog that also likes to be stroked on the chin), she took it. I would say various things, like, 'You are a highly respectable person... you do the best and most original work here... I love you, you know... like a sister.'

I had dignity and earnestness. Always. I was always buying her coffee or crisps from C.'s canteen, and when I went to the bakery I would always bring her something back. I believed that an angel had finally come into my life—or at least a forerunner, who at some point would make me happy.

Money is sweet. It's pleasure. You can never have enough. Money determines your behaviour towards women, your personal life, your personal downtime. There are people who have money and enjoy it and there are others who can't sleep at night. They sit and count their shares, rent, gold sovereigns, property, and anything else that's lucrative. They don't take advice on this, and they stay up all night. Avaricious people are introverted and have many secrets. The miser might have five hundred sovereigns and you only one, and he wants to take it from you. It's not that he needs it, he just wants to take every last thing from others: from anyone, his mother, his father, his grandma. I've not done anything like that, nor have I considered it. God forbid! I would then have needed to visit a psychiatrist from childhood—not at forty years old, when I first went. It was with Eumorphia that I became depressed. Anyway, people visit psychiatrists for many reasons. And they're not all loonies.

I've also been to peep shows and I've repented for it. God is my witness. It didn't do anything for me. That's what they call 'parasexual'. Due to my health problems, mainly because of my heart, the doctors forbade me self-gratification and porn films. I used to prefer masturbation. Now I would tell a young man to find a woman. He'll get nowhere with masturbation. On the contrary, his mind and his nerves will be affected and he'll grow introverted. Masturbation does no good to the young. It's well known.

This morning, with unbearable pain and after a debilitating night also with unbearable pain in which I couldn't sleep a wink, I called the dentist, Mr M., and he received me in his practice at 208 Patission Street.

'They're all rotten, but I can't do anything because of your diabetes. You need to see an oral surgeon. Don't let a dentist lay a hand on you—you'll be wasting your time. Diabetes will get your heart. Beware!'

Then I went to the pharmacy for the pills he prescribed. I only got two of them, though: the third cost forty-three euros and I didn't have the money. Then I returned home and went to sleep to stop the pain. I slept a couple of hours, but I woke up again in great pain. My big sister had made rice pudding, which I love, but I didn't touch it. Incidentally, I take a lot of pills and I wonder for how long I'll need to. I feel a severe pain in my ears, eyes, everywhere. It's like a bullet burrowing deep into me, slowly, penetratingly, without end. Like the knife of a criminal: he jabs it in and out, then in and out again. That's just like the pain in my tooth, the so-called 'toothache'.

That's also just like the pain of a virgin, when (customarily) at twelve years old she is made to sleep with an older man, to take her virginity. That stuff still happens in the Amazon. The girl will take it, she'll hurt, but she won't cry, because her mother has warned her, 'Don't cry: you'll make the bloke believe he has a powerful penis. So don't shriek out. That way you'll humiliate him and he'll think he has some problem. Probably one of size.' (The joyful message of Christ hasn't got there yet.)

I took three painkillers, which, combined with my diabetes, make me drowsy. I'm also shaking a little. But I think I'll overcome all this, God willing.

I wonder why I am in pain. Have I brought bitterness and disappointment to people who helped me? And is God, ever just, apportioning justice 'to every man according to his deeds'? Is He doing it so I don't go to Hell and since 'the last error is worse than the first' and I am tortured forever there without end? Should I toil more for my spiritual survival? All is unalterable—and on a downward spiral. I've never taken a positive action in my life. That has destroyed me psychologically.

I would like to have a house, financial independence, close bonds with certain people—particularly my family. Life, however, is like a chain. The chain holds the boat tight. If it breaks, what's the point in the anchor being dug in well on the seabed? There's no purpose whatsoever. The boat will be dragged off by the waves, struck here and there, and be either sunk or shattered on the rocks. We humans must also be bound tightly to each other. But where have we thrown our anchor? Onto a beautiful girl, perhaps, who's the biggest whore of the lot and doesn't know what she wants, who we naively think is some rock where our anchor can be securely fastened? Just a thought.

'Old-rag pie' was the dish that grandma made us when she would come to our house and see that mother hadn't cooked again. She would roll out thick pastry into the pan, throw in whatever was in the fridge and put it in the oven. It was ready in no time. She also made us fried pieces of bread dipped in egg. I would eat both of them, but I never really liked them. I connected them with my mother's state. From the age of fourteen when I started to earn pocket money from working at the Church printers, I never touched these foods again.

For a meal to be considered a success, four conditions must be met: company, place, environmental factors— i.e., good ventilation or heating, at a distance from the smokers' area—and, finally, the quality of the food. A heavenly meal for me is one which includes: a good portion of moussaka with liberal application of béchamel sauce, large Smyrnian meatballs swimming in sauce, well-roasted meat, chips, fried courgettes with garlic sauce, a large Greek salad, a large portion of taramasalata, along with various kinds of salad, cold beer and buckets of cold water. Sherbet to finish, sticky enough to put in your mouth and glue your tongue to your teeth.

When a woman sees a man having a good time, she'll think either that he has money and he's throwing it around, or that he's beyond cares. Then Beelzebub gets into her, and she thinks, 'Don't worry, I'll take you for a ride and you'll forget food and all the rest.' That's why it's better for a woman not to be around at mealtimes. She always creates problems. 'Don't eat too much, it'll do you no good, you'll lose your figure. Don't forget you've got diabetes…' She's not trying to do you good, she's trying to attract the attention of the other diners, so they all look at her. She doesn't say it because she believes it—she has another motive, and that's the worst thing for a man. It takes away his pleasure.She herself, however, shows no self-restraint. She's a leech. It's always about the others; nothing applies to her. Women use food as a pretext. Many female friends of mine (Greeks, Russians, Ukrainians) have asked me out for a meal, but they always bring up something else: they want me to help with this or that problem of theirs.

'Can you pay my fees for the French Institute?' said one.

'Are you out of your mind?'

She got up and left me just when the food was coming. I ended up with indigestion.

It's better to go out with a friend and keep your head clear. After the meal, women force you to take them home in a taxi. As if I can afford the luxury. They say, 'If you want to go for a meal together, you'll have to borrow money if you don't have it. Then we'll have fun.' That's how they subject you to the ruin of loans. A loan is an embarrassment for a man. It means he cannot support himself. But the woman doesn't care. She says, 'You should have thought before taking it.'

Mussolini said, 'If a man doesn't put on his military uniform and fight, he's not a man; and if a woman doesn't become a mother, she's not a woman.'

Women change face, shape and social position from the moment they give birth. Unmarried women have the whore in them: whores are not only those who open their legs, but more importantly those who try to climb the social ladder and have fun at a man's expense. What can you expect from a woman who isn't fussed about her children, or who doesn't listen to her mother, or who tries to climb the professional ladder in dishonourable ways?

I would never like to take part in a reality TV show. I wouldn't like to exhibit my private life. Every human being has a private life for a third of his day. That is very important and sacred. Reality shows take away a person's dignity. His self-promotion steps up his egotism, and that's not right. I would, however, be happy to take part in a serious TV game show.

I didn't go to some slimming club for a million-drachma prize awarded to whoever lost thirty-five kilos; I went to find some bird to flirt with. But later, even though I'd signed up, I didn't go back—I thought better of it and decided not to sin. I've sinned a thousand times, let's not make it a thousand and one. If you want to slim, you won't manage it with all the clubs in the world, but only by dieting on your own. That's why I didn't go back. Nor do you slim by going to gyms. Roro urged me to go, but I explained to her that you get nothing done there—everyone goes to find a woman. The companies know and exploit that.

(I remember now that once when I went to her house she gave me a massage—clearly, she wanted to get whatever she could from me.)

Today I met the well-known actress Lila Karagatsou at the office of a publisher friend. A stunner. Slightly wrinkled, of course, but let's not forget she's about fifty-five—she's been in the theatre for thirty-five years. Her body is like a North African eel. Angelic. Her face is white and her lips bulge like cherries. Her gaze is like a black poppy. I asked her for an autograph for my little sister and she was more than willing. I thanked her, bid her goodbye like a gentleman and left.

I really believed that something might happen with Marinaki, that she might love me, but at some point she went back to Russia, to the Urals. She had come here under undisclosed circumstances. By aeroplane. She was well-off, I conclude. She was able to live well in her country, but she came here because she thought she could earn a lot of money working in bars. At first a goldsmith had put her up. He tried to pester her into marrying him. But she didn't want to.

She was a beauty. Unfortunately, I have no photos of her—in a moment of passionate rage I tore them all up. She had a body like a long candle, except that it didn't melt. It was permanently alight, permanently incandescent and imperious. If you didn't know her, you would think she was a virginal creature, that she hadn't even been touched by a cat's paw. But you can never know the history of a Russian woman. I met her through a Greek friend of mine, C. I remember that the first day we met she was very beaten up, with bruises across her forehead and a deep scar on her neck. Her leg was in bandages and she was hobbling. C. told me that the goldsmith was responsible. The day before, he had asked her to marry him but she refused. Since he felt humiliated, he paid two henchmen to beat her up. They put her in a car, took her to some dark street off Syngrou, opened the door and bundled her out like a sack of potatoes. Marinaki survived. By her good fortune, some Russians were passing at that moment and they picked her up and took her straight to hospital. My friend C. told me all this and it broke my heart. I gave Marinaki all the money I had on me that day. Thereafter, every day we met, I would give her what I could. We got on well; I made her feel good again. We went on a lot of trips and excursions to monasteries.

Our relationship remained platonic, just hugging and kissing—I didn't want to sin again. I just didn't want to. If I'd screwed her, it would then be difficult to cut it off: we were too close. She was a good girl and Greece wasn't kind to her. She looked for work here for four years—even as a cleaner by the end. She had repented and didn't want to fall back into sin. I bought her some ecclesiastical books in Russian. She read them and she prayed, and I think that by her last year here she had given up prostitution. I thought she became more beautiful then. From the beginning I realised that she was a prostitute, but in the final months, when I saw her, I had the impression she was going up and up into Heaven and that I couldn't reach her— she had become a pure, ethereal being. I believe that woman could give a man not just drops but whole spoonfuls of pleasure with her hands—no one could taste that food twice. (You enjoy good food once only.)

Marinaki was a lady (Eumorphia couldn't even touch her little finger). She was a prostitute, yes, but not a whore. Besides, when a prostitute repents and returns to the straight and narrow, she is purified. We have the examples of Mary Magdalene and Mary of Egypt. And so many others.

Once I went for coffee with her and her friend Claudia. At some point, I thought of something and became sad. My spirits fell. The two of them then got up and kissed me simultaneously, one on each cheek. At that moment I felt that I had jumped out of an aeroplane with a parachute and flew up instead of down. I still have the intense feeling of those hot kisses on my cheeks. A man must try everything in order to have a past, as the great singer Yannis Parios says. No woman touched me like Marinaki. I remember us eating together in a taverna and the proprietor came over and said, 'Mate, when are you going to introduce me to a woman like yours?'

'Where will I find another one?'

Yes. I loved that woman a lot. I liked her games, her sweet talk. 'You're an angel sent by God. What would I do without you?'

She might have said so because I had given her a hundred and thirty thousand drachmas, saying 'I don't want it back. It's from my heart.' And then she hugged me sweetly and kissed me, biting my lips. I felt like an athlete who'd just won gold. That's passion for you. If I did wrong, gentlemen, sue me!

Then, however, she found some fellow countryman of hers, named Yuri. He didn't suit her in the slightest and I'm sure she didn't love him, but something funny was going on: she must have had some obligation to him.

Marinaki, on the other hand, was devoted to me. I know that. Even the fact that she didn't invite me to

her leaving do with her friends, just before she left—
even that moves me. She did it because she didn't want
to hurt me… nor hurt herself. Anyway, that night she
said to everyone, 'Chrysovalantis treated me better
even than my mother.' I found that out later from her
friend Claudia and I was deeply touched that Marinaki
said such a thing about me.

She was a person with sensibilities. At some point
she said, 'You are the only man in my life who I've said
sorry to twice.'

Once on Aegina, she kissed me three or four times,
and I insisted on more but she refused, so I became
very upset with her. She said, 'I'm off!' and indeed she
got up and left. Then I searched over the whole island
for her and eventually when I found her, she apologised and said, 'I was selfish.'

The second time was in the Neon Café in Syntagma, when she persuaded me to sign a paper that
she worked as a cleaner at our house. I emphatically
refused, and she didn't talk to me for an hour, but later
she regretted it and apologised.

I once said to Old Nick: 'On Sunday I'm going for coffee with my friend K.'

'Right, so you have a better friend than me?' he
asked, irate. He wanted exclusivity. He wanted me to
think only about him and his company from morning
to night. And on top of that he called me an idiot. Of
course, I didn't say anything, I just looked at him

askance, implying, 'You're a useless old fart.' I don't want to argue, nor is it in my nature to squabble. Even in his case I said to myself, 'Are you really going to have it out with a nutcase?'

Father Nikolaos (a saintly man) said, 'There are two of us and we're arguing. I leave. Who will the other chap argue with?' He considered diplomacy a means of survival.

But I'm afraid. I'm afraid something will happen to me. When I get angry and shout, my heart starts racing and I feel an intense tremor through my whole body and my blood sugar skyrockets. Plus the fact that I only want others to see me smiling. Arguing is not part of my life. But now that I think about it, perhaps that's the reason for my failure—I was always the punch bag. Yes.

Everyone says, 'Chrysovalantis? Who takes any notice of that wet blanket? Even if you rip him off he'll say "thanks".' And yes, they started ripping me off, once or twice, until it became the norm. If I had money, I would have isolated myself, I would have gone far from all those rogues. I would have concerned myself with art only: I would have gone to the National Opera. There I could practise my diplomatic capabilities (without coming to harm), as so many—so many—monks from Athos have told me I have. Yes, one of them told me that chess was invented by a German king who didn't want to see his officers continually getting their swords out to settle their differences. He therefore created chess so that the justice of skill would prevail over the justice of the blade.

One Saturday morning I was having coffee with Marinaki. I had just loaned her twenty thousand drachmas. She gave me a lovely, intoxicating kiss and said, 'Thank you.' I fell into a haze and asked for a second and third and fifth and tenth. At the eleventh she lost her rag and started shouting.

'Why did you lend me the money? To fuck me? You're as bad as the others!'

I practically started crying. Can a woman humiliate me like that? Like an officer deprived of his rank by court-martial, his ribbons stripped from him in front of his troops. I felt a pricking in my eyes and a chill inside me. My heart felt like it was about to burst. I blushed. Sweated.

'Come on, let me kiss you,' she said, for she was very astute. She kissed me and said sorry.

I kissed her back. I forgave her at once, since I believe that after some friction, when the woman herself embraces you and kisses your lips, it means that she really is repentant and that it's not a Judas kiss. Her lips dry your teary eyes. I forgave her, and that was one of the last battlefields on which I fought and won.

What value do a soldier's stripes have if he sits inside an office? He needs to be out in the field. I said '*one* of the last battlefields', but not the last battlefield.

For if I say that, I will feel that I've retired from the field entirely. Who? Me? The fighter?

Yes, but where will I find another Marinaki? A woman, an unbelievable woman like that! I took her everywhere, always to cafés with sofas in the corner. I kissed her, hugged her, massaged her back and arms. I was as sweet as could be, even on the telephone.

'Kisses, my darling, sweet kisses. Sending lots of sweet kisses, Marinaki!'

'Da, keeses. Da, keeses.'

I don't think that a Russian man could give a Russian woman such love, irrespective of whether they have the same means of expressing emotion. Russian women want it, but their fellow countrymen are cold. That's why they come to these Mediterranean countries—to feel our warmth. The warmth is not only the weather, it's also human and emotional.

Russian men beat their women—hard. They have three failings: they're pig-headed, they're drunkards, and they beat their wives. Ukrainians are the same but worse. In general, all of the Soviet leftovers are like this.

What should I do, Marinaki? Die?

I believe that in time Marinaki will come back. But I hope to be married by then. If I'm married, I won't divorce (let's clear that up now) but I would cheat on my spouse with Marinaki. Even though it's not really cheating.

My big sister says to me, 'Stay away from women—women have no good intentions with you.'

The doctor who looks after me at the Tzaneio Hospital says pretty much the same. 'Better to stay at home rather than go out with a woman. She'll be up to no good.'

I must uphold that conviction to save myself. I now know that women are rapacious. Like hell they'd be interested in my shapely body, my piety or my virtues. I'm just worried about one thing: they'll get their hands on my house.

Marinaki and I used to go shopping a lot. I bought her various things, among them a bracelet. That's a classic gift of mine: I do it to all the women with whom I'm developing a semi-romantic relationship. To tell the truth, I have a cunning scheme in mind. As in America they make their convicts wear bracelets to identify them—well, I buy bracelets for all the women I love, so that they remember me.

I got her loads of stuff: skirts, dresses, jackets, bags, make-up, vitamins and lotions for her body, along with lots of other things.

One day her bloke had ripped her bra and she complained to me. I went off immediately and replaced it twofold. I bought her a lovely purple set: a three-quarter bra with a thong. It was lovely. I bought her a white bra as well. The former from Ermou Street and the latter from her neighbourhood—Kallithea. And yes, when I bought her something, I always received my kiss in return. Marinaki was a good girl, she wasn't like those other smutty ones.

I wanted to write her a poem with a kangaroo in. I thought of her as a kangaroo. Once I hugged her so tightly that she said, 'Why are you hugging me so long?'

'I'm holding you like a mummy kangaroo holds the little kangaroo in her pouch,' I replied.

'Really?'

'I'll take you, put you in my belly and run away. I don't care where.'

She laughed. She loved the things I said. She was a warm woman, and she became hotter as the day wore on. Anyone who came near her was burned.

That Yuri who wanted to marry her hated me, because he saw the love and interest that Marinaki had for me. He reacted strangely.

Once or twice when I saw him he didn't even say 'Good morning' to me, nor did he give me a second glance. Like I was a worm and he was the king! Those old Russian commies are like that.

Marinaki, on the other hand, was a diplomat. A different character altogether. I didn't say anything to her about his pig-headed Russian behaviour because, firstly, I didn't want to get involved—I didn't want to come between them—and secondly, I didn't know what dealings they had among themselves.

Now I've got more experience and I know. Let others make their own way. As long as I'm alright. It would be nice if she comes back and I have her in my arms again and take her wherever she wants. That would be nice. Hope dies last. First goes Chrysovalantis, then Marinaki, and only after that, Chrysovalantis' hope. After. Long after.

Many people went on at me about Marinaki: 'Leave! Can't you see she's taking advantage?'

I didn't believe them. *I* was the beggar, not Marinaki. I took her hand in mine and said, 'Marinaki, let's go here, let's go there.'

She was a gentle woman, very tall (one metre seventy-nine) and beautiful. She often took me to her home, where I would kiss her, stroke her tenderly, massage her. When she saw I was gloomy, she would say, 'Don't worry that your body gets tired. Don't worry'—always with love, kind words and her own kind of dignity. Marinaki had dignity.

At first, when she didn't know me, she was very guarded. She was afraid she'd have another situation like with the goldsmith. But then she grew accustomed to me. I loved her so much and at the cafés where we went, everyone would say 'Good morning,' not to me but to Marinaki. Now no one says anything.

We would begin our meetings with espresso and move on to a taverna. The only thing I noticed was that when she was drunk (and she liked a tipple) she didn't want to kiss me. Strange. I know that if a woman gets drunk, she let's herself go. Marinaki did the opposite.

I sweet-talked her, I stroked her, I lifted her up in the air. I took her to the supermarket and filled up her fridge. I did that twice—even though I didn't have enough money to be doing it.

Life is tough and a man needs a woman in his life to soften it. I am terrified by the thought that I might remain on my own.

'Careful you don't stay unmarried,' my psychiatrist friend says. I want to have a companion, to make a home with a woman. To be able to fornicate. At some point I'll lose the ability. The diabetes has got me down there. Yes.

I'll never forget Marinaki and how tenderly she treated me. I can't say the same for the others—particularly Eumorphia, the love of my life.

I tread this path alone
It's alone I make my way
Black fate has struck me down
That's why I'm ill alway'.

I was sitting with a colleague in a café in Chalandri when to my displeasure I realised that it was Albanian owned and run. The Albanians and the Russians have taken our cafés. This society is going to be transformed much quicker than we imagine. The only thing we haven't seen is them on the TV presenting the news and other programmes. I don't know what we're coming to.

I don't go on holiday. Firstly, because with the situation at home I can't be away for long; secondly, because I don't have much spare cash; thirdly, because I can't bear the tourist stampedes on the Greek islands. In particular, I can't bear the places where the English go. To provoke the locals, they go around with their pants down outside the bars, and some of them take to rather exhibitionist practices. The most mild case (can you believe it?!) is nudity on beaches—the notorious 'naturism'. When I need the toilet or have a shower in my bathroom, I have nothing to be ashamed of. But on a beach I'd be embarrassed. Dozens of eyes would suddenly turn to me. If it were a private beach or my own swimming pool where I wouldn't scandalise anyone, then sure, I would swim in the nude. But there's no way I could do so on organised nudist beaches. I would feel deficient, because everyone would be looking at me. I mean, they would look and they would comment. Yes. They would comment on my rolls. Besides, I would never want a tender young girl or woman (single or married) to be scandalised on account of me. You shouldn't feed rotten grass to sheep.

A question related to Old Nick's partner: did she really have two incidents on Panepistimiou Street—one nasty and one strange—and is that why she still considers that street unlucky?

The first time, so she says, they stole her bag, and as they yanked its strap she dislocated her shoulder.

The second time, she was waiting at the traffic lights and a man in a suit, a dead ringer for Hitchcock, came up to her. He looked at her and said, 'What do you want with me, babe?' She turned in surprise and asked, 'Who are you, sir, and why are you talking like that?'

He replied angrily, 'It's your fault, you bitch, that I can't hold down a man.'

I confess that since I found that out, even though I didn't really believe it, I've been more careful on Panepistimiou Street.

Old Nick bragged that that they get up to all sorts of debauched, passionate love-making. They each still provide the other—after thirty-five years of marriage—with the unquenched flame of erotic passion. If that's true, beats me. How can someone with so many problems—someone who has put half of Athens and half of Thessaloniki in the gutter, who is wanted by all the banks and a couple of hundred lawyers—how can he make love, not to mention of that kind and quality? Is he not psychologically affected? Is he so desensitised? My big sister told me that both of them are objects of psychiatric study, but especially him. She understood who he was when he started sending me legal threats one after another, which (as I found out later) weren't written by a lawyer but by himself: he put his work to one side and wrote those threats.

'I don't owe you a penny… You've no right to be on my back… You've no right to slander me… you're going against the company's interests... You're obstructing the work of your colleagues...'

He even manipulated my little sister, who was recovering from her stroke. He found her alone at home and gave her a document to sign, which he said was for receipt of one of the many threat letters he brought me. She believed him and signed. Later we realised that the fraudster had made her sign a receipt of payment that said he had given me all the money he owed and that he had paid off his debts. The creep! But I don't have money to throw around going after some idiot. Besides, our excellent lawyer Mr Argyropoulos told me that he gathered (from a correspondence they had), that he took delight in being pursued.

After all that, he had the gall (I'm disclosing this for the first time) to call me on my mobile and ask for assistance in finding clients. Can you believe it?!

I think that Greeks don't love their children as much as the Finns. The Finns are tender and sensitive—and sweet. It's like they're talking to their second heart. Moreover, when an English person speaks to their child—and generally to their fellow human—he might seem cold, but in reality, he is not. Studies have been carried out on the matter.

Unfortunately, things are different in Greece. If I'm with a friend in a café, for example in Syntagma Square, and at some point—to show my love—I get up and kiss him or stroke his arm, everyone will take it the wrong way. This despite the fact that it would be a kiss of love, a touch of the soul, the tangible reciprocation of a unique friendship.

If I do that to a female friend, they'll say, 'The crafty bugger, the fatty, going for that innocent girl.' I'll be seriously misinterpreted by my fellow Greeks because we've all become exhibitionist studs and made fornication our life goal, rather than spiritual communication, as the Gospel tells us. And we've been left without sensitivity and with no inclination towards communication with our fellow man. You can't look someone in the eye anymore and give them a visual caress. You can't pay a girl a tender compliment. Romanticism and the quiet life are considered conservative: they're a démodé family mentality.

I, humble Chrysovalantis, set myself against that with all of my small power, and I become a wandering old fool: a sensitive, sweet fool trying to approach the world.

I don't approach a girl by grabbing her breasts, but by stroking her softly on the back of her hand—the part displayed for touch, not even the underside—and I say, 'I got this for you' (some nice bracelet or a serious book).

If she's blonde, she normally responds, 'Thank you, Chrysovalantis, I'll keep the gift so as not to offend you, but you've played and lost with me.' Brunettes are the worst, since they let me give them something, then something else, and they only reject me at the end, so I succumb to grief and heartache.

At least I had Marinaki in my life to make me feel like a man. Eumorphia made me feel like a chimpanzee. And Roro, a taxi driver—Athens-Sparta, Pangrati-Syntagma and so forth.

> *Loneliness and desolation*
> *Will make me run away*
> *And cut a beech tree down*
> *And burn it day by day.*

I have to say that I've got another worry: with my diabetes I have suffered neurological inertia. I used to work until ten or eleven in the evening and I could still go out to eat afterwards. Now I'm tired from four or five in the afternoon and I want to go home to rest. That's become a necessity. There's no way I'm going to announce that to my new company. Never. Let me suffer, let me bleed, let the wound pour forth blood. I will never tell them, because ultimately, I realised that not all people are sensitive and emotionally intelligent. There are some monsters, who kick you when you're down and throw you off the cliff. And they enjoy it too.

I don't want to think, newly appointed in the job as I am, that I might find such people there. I haven't yet explored the workplace, to see if the employees are

Greeks or if a foreign, destructive invasion has taken place. That is my great concern. With the bosses and the other employees I have come into contact with, so far so good. I will try to keep things in balance. I am in dire need. The bigger the boat, the more we load it. So, for me, the greater the financial need I exhibit, the more they'll put on my back. I will, therefore, keep my boat small. Yes.

My parents and sisters were delighted, as well as two friends of mine who I informed. They were pleased, and I was pleased, too.

One day, long ago, when I was working for Old Nick down in the basement, he phoned me and shouted, 'Come up urgently!'

Oh dear, I thought, what's happened now? I ran upstairs. His expression was grave, and that worried me even more.

'It's about your future.'

He's going to fire me, I thought. I went pale.

'Everyone of your age has children in high school, and you're still unmarried.'

'But… I never found the right…'

'Where do you think you'll find her? On Mount Athos? In the cafés you go to with your OAP friends to drink barley?'

'But…'

'No buts! Go to the Mouzakis Thread Factory in one hour, when all the women will be leaving work.

Go up behind one that you like and say, "You can see me, darling, this is who I am. I'll take you if you'll take me." Now, go! Get a move on!'

Early the next morning he called me in.

'What happened?'

'Nothing...'

'I bet you were too embarrassed to speak... Go now and make a sign that says, "I want a woman to marry." Then go again today and stand outside the factory. Someone's bound to approach you.'

I burst out laughing. 'Good joke!'

'You dare to laugh at the things I say to you, you oaf?'

He went bright red, thumped his desk and wheeled around. The whole floor of the office stared at us.

I went into a spin. I lowered my head and left in a hurry.

I made the sign and stood outside the factory, because I even thought him capable of following me and if he twigged that I hadn't done what he told me, he would fire me. But I went to a corner so I couldn't be easily seen. I didn't make too much of a fool of myself. Thankfully, the next day he had forgotten and didn't mention it again. Anyway, I was worried for a long time afterwards that he would lose his temper again.

I hope I don't have that kind of boss again. Ever.

At this point I can't help but think about Madame Eumorphia. I feel sick just saying the name. It hurts my teeth. A hysteria takes hold of me, pounding my ears, teeth and head. That woman was a taker. I don't think anyone could really love her. She always lived in hypocrisy and deceit.

Show your neighbour your real value and he will respect it. He won't buy you. You don't need to be gold. Show him you're hematite, or a pebble (a pure one, mind), and he'll put you in his pebble box. All of that was by-the-by to her ladyship. She wanted me to sign for a three-bed apartment just like that. She's the other side of Old Nick. He thought he was clever and every-one else stupid, and she considered herself cleverer than the cleverest women.

A small vignette of a revolutionary act of mine today: 7.30 pm. I enter my home. The telephone rings. It's the bank.

'Can I call you back in a bit?'

'No!'

'My good lady,' I said, 'I will call you back, I can't talk at the moment.'

'OK, I'll wait.'

At five past eight the telephone rings again and it's the same unpleasant voice.

'You have an outstanding debt of one thousand six hundred euros.'

'I'm aware of that.'

'What are you doing about it?'

'I'll give you two hundred now, since I am just out

of unemployment, and in a couple of months you'll have the rest.'

'Oh, so you've even made a plan?'

'Why are you being sarcastic?'

'I'm not being sarcastic at all. I'm being polite, sir.'

'You aren't being polite at all. You're being sarcastic. I have diabetes, heart problems and, more importantly, I'm a long-standing customer of yours. You can't talk to me like this. Give me your name, please, I will send a letter of complaint.'

She wouldn't give it to me.

'Give it to me.'

'No.'

In the end she gave it to me, but I was so worked up that I hung up in her face. After about a quarter of an hour, however, because of my sensitivity—or perhaps because I spoke sharply to a female being—I called her back and apologised.

'You know, I'm a child of the Church. That's not normally my manner.'

'I'm the same,' she said, and we made up.

'You'll deposit those two hundred euros though, yes?'

'Of course. It's my moral duty to do so.'

I had an even worse experience with the other bank —may God strike it down! After the unacceptable way in which they treated me, whenever I hear of a robbery at that bank I feel a ripple of pleasure. They use their employees as levers and extort money like pimps.

I found out that my new boss said to the director of the company, 'Chrysovalantis seems an excellent chap and he'll prove useful to us.'

What's more, I'm officially hired. I couldn't believe it would happen so fast.

Therefore, either he has information from outside— from the marketplace—that I know my work, and that I'm not a fraud and don't take commissions, or he has an excellent eye from his lengthy experience.

I have a problem with the blood vessels of the penis, due to my diabetes, and I don't know what to do. I have a stinging sensation after I pee. It's shrunk, too— I don't know how to deal with this. My erection isn't all there—it's at half-mast. That's why I have stopped falling in love and pestering women. I don't have the sexual stimulus. It's one thing to know you're hard, and quite another to know you can't get it up.

I feel like a soldier who has lost the battle. Yes.

> *Oh, pained heart of mine*
> *Pained soul of mine*
> *How can you take any more*
> *In this hard life?*
> *Take up your cross*
> *And look after yourself.*

Yet another suffering poet. Unfortunately.

Today I finally received my company's business cards. I've been working my socks off for them for two weeks without being paid, but at least they hired me immediately. I trust that my friends and acquaintances will help me bring some work to the company.

I discovered table football at the age of eleven. I would go to a place called Aroma, in my local square. It was owned by a certain Mr Kostas, a short, thin man of about fifty with a crooked nose and a big moustache. He must have been a pothead—he always looked stoned I would sweep or wash up and he let me play for free. Once, when the place was empty and I was putting the dustpan and brush away in the cupboard, he approached me from behind. He was emitting a very strange smell. Suddenly I felt a hot sucking sensation on my neck. A voice inside me screamed 'No!' I ducked and slipped out between his legs. I ran away and never set foot there again.

I still don't frequent any cafés in my neighbourhood. I don't want to see all those idiotic, vile people, who would probably make some comment about me, calling me pathetic or ridiculous. Those creeps, opportunists, exploiters of helpless women and innocent children—I hate them. They're dangerous scum and they can lay into you for no reason whatsoever.

I went to see an old client of mine, a complete nutcase. She's forty or forty-five but she looks thirty. I felt really at ease with her. We chatted, she placed a large order, she lauded me on my professionalism... not to say flirted with me.

She treated me to a sweet coffee and it was like nectar from Zeus' chalice. We had a warm, polite goodbye. When I left this most lovely and amiable of ladies, I felt like the old monk thrown out of his cell and left homeless by a nasty abbot.

When I'm at work or with friends or at church, I forget my hunger. The doctor insists I go out and see people so that I'm ashamed if they observe me eating like a pig. If I'm having a good time, the hunger leaves my mind. Eating too much is a bad habit. It should disappear from the whole spectrum of the galactic system. If I eat a lot, my blood sugar sky-rockets. I've noticed that when I'm at home I am continually eating—out of momentum. Always. Sometimes I feel that I'll be sick if I eat more, but I still go on, especially when the others start arguing.

I need to escape from platonic love and move onto its fleshy equivalent. It's a pleasing sight, two bodies that match and bond and soil the sheets, leaving their stamp—the sign that two people who loved each other were there. Does the woman draw the man into bed or the other way around, I ask myself? I conclude that it's the woman that draws the man, for she lies down first, opens her legs wide like an endless tunnel of sexual exploration and says to him, 'Come inside and explore.' She doesn't say everything, she deliberately leaves some things in the shadows, thinking, 'Let the idiot look for himself. Let's see what he'll find in there.' The man looks and goes deep in and the woman, if she wants, gives it to him. If she doesn't want, she doesn't give.

Women enjoy ninety percent of the pleasure in sex. Nonetheless, pleasure and orgasm are separate. You come to an orgasm primarily for yourself. Some married women, however, give orgasms to other people, too, and they do it to punish their husbands. That's a philosophy that has unsettled me. What role does a woman play with her husband? Can she hold his hand and give him love? The man tries to undress quickly and get her into bed, while she thinks how she can play with him. She thinks of herself as a cat playing with a dazed mouse: she has it in her hands and does whatever she wants with it. Since the poor thing is also drunk, it becomes doubly mad.

I'm in a lot of pain. I took another painkiller, the third since the morning. I'm being tested. Previously, I would suffer only from my kidneys or from love. Now it's toothache. I am worried every time I go home about what kind of night I will have. How will I be tonight? Like I was yesterday, or the night before, when I couldn't sleep a wink? If all the roots don't come out, there's no way I can rest.

'Lord, remember me when thou comest into thy kingdom, now and always.'

We ask God to remember us. I ask him to help me sleep. Last night I didn't get a wink. I took more painkillers and went into a stupor, but still the pain didn't go away.

Despite that, I wrote a little ditty this morning,

> *Oh that I never drink again*
> *The unbearable water of this pain*
> *Better to cross a thousand pits of death*
> *Than to be tortured thus again.*

I'm extremely tired. I wouldn't want to analyse the poem now.

It's possible that a woman would mitigate my bodily and spiritual pain. Even if she were married and had children. I'm also a child. She'd practically be changing my nappy; giving me a nice massage all over my body.

I'm English in my head, French in my politeness, Russian in my heart and Greek in my clothes. I adore the precision of the English in punctuality, money, payment—everything. The Swedes are next. Don't go near the Mediterraneans in financial matters.

I'm a Russian in my heart because I'm an amorous old thing and Russians fall in love very easily. This didn't always work out well, I'll admit. My French politeness was at fault, of course. It is often misinterpreted by the cunning Southerners and many other races.

I loathe the rudeness, insensitivity and pig-headedness of the Russians as much as I love and admire the punctiliousness of the English. If a Russian judges —on his own terms—that he shouldn't talk to you, there's no way he will do so, no matter how hard you try. It's the notorious Russian stubbornness. If, moreover, a Russian deems that he should ask you for a loan of thirty euros and sees you're a sensitive chap, he will ask you in front of everyone. And money loaned is money spent. There's no way he'll give it back to you. You're more likely to get a kiss from a member of the Taliban than loaned money back from a Russian.

On Monday I have to go to three large publishers. I hope they find my offers attractive. Then I'll get my few cents.

Should I be stricter with myself? Rein myself in? My diabetes has made me insecure in the face of society. I think I need to be stricter and to remove some people from my life, or adopt a woman's mentality. We'll see. Everything is in motion, as Heraclitus said.

My toothache recurs and gets me down. I think that perhaps it's God boxing my ears, as the Fathers say, to show me that my sins will send me to Hell. Even if you have made a truckload of mistakes, however, if God sees a grain of repentance, He'll say, 'Enter thou into the joy of thy Lord.'

Will the Omnipotent One show the same mercy to insignificant me?

I used to tell lies, but not serious ones.

A well-constructed lie can be told by a lawyer in court and destroy a needy family, or by a very literate man to confuse an illiterate one into signing some document. My lies were not of that kind. Besides, I told them more often than not for a joke. (Lying in a romantic relationship is different again, since it is ninety percent a way of justifying yourself, and ten percent a deception of the other).

Moreover, I would lie to get myself out of trouble. For example, when I was late for work because I was taking pills and couldn't wake up, I would say, 'The bus broke down,' or, 'I had no money and I came on foot.'

Nonetheless, my confessors insisted 'Satan is the father of deceit.'

I remember a very serious incident with the bank: I had made a settlement but didn't pay it, as I had no money. I said that I had lost the papers and forgotten the dates. In the end, however, I was forced to pay a hundred and forty thousand drachmas just on interest. I seriously messed up. Then I thought that in Greece you only learn if you pay. Isn't that what happened with almost all my women? They took what they wanted from me and then cast me out.

Madame Eumorphia, for example—I wish her well (one mustn't swear, after all)—made a fool of me. She asked me for all kinds of things as if it were nothing. For me, that was fuel to the fire of love, since you don't ask favours like that from any old bloke. It gave me something to hold on to, and I was led more and more astray and passion overcame me.

Well, I ended up at the psychiatrist and I was forced to take a number of pills, which aggravated my health and caused organ malfunctions. The pills brought on headaches, drowsiness and side effects with my erection. I developed an unprecedented and unchecked priapism. I couldn't walk down the street. My diabetes came from the pills, too, I think.

Eumorphia, therefore, is also responsible for my diabetes. I attribute a hundred percent of moral accountability to her. For when an organism doesn't burst, doesn't shout, doesn't have any relief, it turns in on itself and serious damage is done. Yes.

My father hated lies. He always said, 'Sincerity is one of the most important virtues.' Once when I broke a lamp and told him that Jack had knocked it over, he grabbed the peppermill from the kitchen and emptied it all onto my tongue. 'I won't beat you this time,' he said. A few days later Jack really did pull up all the roses in the garden and then disappeared from the face of the earth. I'm certain that my father did something to that dog, but I never asked.

I wrote a poem on the bus. A daring poem. I'm afraid that I've committed a great sin by writing it and that those who read it will sin also.

Its title is 'Eumorphia's Sorrow'.

> *Wild ferret of mine*
> *Get into her hard and true*
> *And if she has a good old time*
> *Give her a Fanta, too.*
>
> *It's no great crime*
> *Nor even is it a sin*
> *To drink my tasty juice*
> *And get it all in.*
>
> *So be a good girl*
> *Don't keep on like this*
> *In the silence of the night*
> *Let me treat you right,*
> *Let me stroke the puss-puss*
> *While you fondle the pears.*
>
> *I'll take you to the hill*
> *I'll take you to the fjord*
> *I'll get frill-a-lil-lil*
> *And you'll get your reward.*

Now I don't know, I'm embarrassed and feel very guilty. I think that this poem will get a lot of people into trouble because of me. It's like the drug-dealer and the addict: both are committing a sin. Yes, I lived a wanton life in the past. But now that I'm recovering, should I be thinking about that kind of thing again? What will I tell my confessor tomorrow? That I've written a porno-poem? He'll forbid me from taking communion. Passion has cast me into sin again. Perhaps the lack of masturbation is to blame, or the fact that I haven't had sexual intercourse with a woman for a significant period of time. I don't know. The fact is that I'm going to fall headlong into Hell.

After I turned seventeen I started to swear: 'wanker', 'wankshaft', 'wankadoodle', 'Mr Wankster', that sort of thing. I didn't use more serious swearwords because of my family. I was afraid that if I became used to saying them, they would slip out at home and then there'd be hell to pay. My family would never swear. I mean, my mother and the girls. I admit that my father used to swear at his father-in-law. 'Like hell I'll call him "General", that good-for-nothing ranker'. We didn't see that side of the family much.

I feel serious regret now. How can I sleep at night? My pillow is the judge of my day and my prayer is the night-watchman. God is merciful, but also just, and He dispenses justice to each 'according to his deeds'. I mean, my toothache surely means that I have committed—or uttered—sins. Yes.

Now the pain has gripped me again, despite taking very strong pills. I think that salvation awaits, however, because I'm going to have oral surgery on Thursday. It will last hours and the aftermath will be very difficult. My mouth needs to remain closed so that bacteria don't get in. I'm worried about how it will go, because with my diabetes I don't know if the wounds will close. My little sister will be coming with me.

It's time to fall in love again. When I fall in love, I'm like a car without a steering wheel. That's why the song goes, 'I'll remember you like a crazy lorry.' I'm really in the mood for love. Perhaps it's because I found work. Love with no money is like sitting at a table piled with plates, all of which are empty.

How will I tell my confessor that on the one hand I'm writing filth and on the other I'm chanting at the psalter? How will I dare? OK, you'll tell me that my filthy writing is how I blow off steam. Better to do that, then, than fall into greater sin.

Every move my mother makes, every word she says, brims with kindness and humanity. A virtuous nun in mad Manhattan.

At work there is a beautiful and obliging secretary with a lovely body. Her name is Maria. But I'm going to be prudent. That girl is not for me. She's only just twenty. How would I come across? The grandpa who wears his foustanella inside out and is prepared to put it on for a war of passion? Anyway, I'm not the sort of creep to force myself onto the girl and violate her body.

Yesterday as we were leaving, she offered to drop me off in the city centre in her car. I refused, for obvious reasons. I don't want to start the same old things again and destroy myself. I don't want to be seen at work drooling after a girl. I want to keep myself in check.

A new life, a new start, a new path
Without a sin or a lusty glance.

I'm afraid and I keep away from fire. I'm no fire-man. I'm not keen on the other six girls at work: they're all short and fat and cold. Simpletons. It's like they're sextuplets. Maria, though, is tender and warm. She came in today with a burn on her left hand. I wanted to say, 'Can I get you a lotion to make it better?' But I was afraid she would say yes. And what would the boss say if he opened the door and saw me stroking her hand? Good luck persuading him afterwards that it was a health issue! He would think, 'The fatty is fondling the little girl,' and he would fire me as an example to the others.

I've not yet become the Athenian Rasputin. After a scandal comes all the chitter-chatter and through chitter-chatter comes slander.

Maria says to me, 'Do you want paper? A pen? A rubber?' and I look at her legs, which are shapely with lovely curves. Her behind is rather perky and has a naturally bulbous shape. I hope that her work doesn't do her harm, because many secretaries get cellulite from sitting down, and problems with their core and their neck.

There were two people in Old Nick's company who from the moment that I set foot there, waged war on me. The first was P., the director of production, who considered me a serious competitor and thought I would take his position. As if! I neither cared nor ever contested anything. But he was a very insecure person. He realised that he didn't even have a tenth of my knowledge and that's why he always undermined and disparaged me.

I mentioned two people before, but now I can't remember the second. My diabetes does this to me. Unless I've since forgiven him and I can't remember. I hope so. It's true, I often suffer these dimmings. (Glimmering is when the light strengthens, dimming is when it dims.)

Ah, I've remembered! The second person was Mopface. As I've already mentioned, she was a hideous old hag, never been shagged in her life, four foot tall with five-inch heels on. She was good at her job, but a witch. She continually flustered me and burdened me emotionally, as she didn't let me near Eumorphia. When I managed to, she would send me on urgent errands which she had apparently just remembered. She was a devilish Mopface. I should stress here that I'm not a racist: it wasn't her ugliness that annoyed me, but her character. She was always quarrelsome, rude, sarcastic, with the lowest kind of humour, which she would often use against her colleagues, not excepting me. They say that unloved women are cranky. This isn't always the case, to put it bluntly. Single women who have never whored themselves are not bad. On the contrary (it's well known), their hearts brim with love and kindness. But Mopface...

There were others, too, that persecuted me in the company. I remember rascals such as M., B. and F., who would set fire to me at any opportunity. They poured napalm on a poor boy with a naked soul— without a shield nor even fireproof clothing. And their patron, Givashit, would come in afterwards and lay into me, too. A couple of times I couldn't take it and I started crying I was so upset.

Another time I started crying was during the great bust-up between the two partners, Old Nick and Givashit. I had bound ten copies by hand of a rare publication by the Benaki Museum for Old Nick. I put my soul into making those things, to the point that I went especially to Kiokpasoglou's Bookbinders in Koropi.

I came back late in the afternoon to the company, knackered. Just when I entered the lift to go upstairs, Givashit intercepted me at the door and said,

'I'll be taking those. I need them.'

'But the boss wants them, he sent me to have them made. He's expecting them from me urgently.'

'Don't worry, give them to me.'

'But please,' I said and then he started yelling, but I mean really yelling. I shrank away and fled up to Old Nick's office like a rain-drenched cat. He saw my empty hands and he started yelling, too.

'Where are the books I asked you for?'

'Your partner took them from me.'

And then the wretch, the chicken, instead of giving hell to the other chap, said to me,

'OK, as soon as he's gone, go to Koropi again and make me ten more copies.'

I started crying. I felt like a sheep whose shepherd had abandoned him to the wolves. He wasn't a hard-nosed businessman, that one.

Not to mention that he always insulted holy things. That really worked me up. Once when his filthy mouth brazenly said, 'Go fuck the Vir—, go fuck Jes—,' it riled me so much that I threw the papers out of my hands and made straight for the exit.

He sent a couple of colleagues to find me, thinking that I'd gone to drown myself in the Kifissos. In fact, I'd gone to the sandwich shop and bought a triple special and a beer and baklava with lashings of syrup. I was sitting and eating when I saw L. and R. pacing along the road in a panic, looking for me. I called out, 'Come and have a cold beer.'

'Good Lord, are you completely mad? We've been going up and down the river to see where you had jumped in, and you're sitting here munching away!'

First, he treated me in his usual way and then he pretended he was worried about me and sent these two to look for me. I'm certain that he did it to give me a crisis of conscience and see how much I could endure. Meanwhile, the hypocrite had a large icon of St. Demetrios of Thessaloniki in his office. 'The saint protects me from evil people,' he would say, and I would just stop myself from saying, 'It would be better for it to guard you from yourself.'

I'm always writing poetry these days. I'm on form. I'm inspired.

> I write verse and bear arms
> For some lost dreams
> But the times will change
> And you'll return, unclothed
> And you'll secretly come upon
> My dicky and me.

The external jobs that my boss sends me to do aren't enough to earn a wage. I think that God will help me. I'm concerned. Some of my clients will need to support me. I've started to worry. He says to me, 'The good ones won't leave the company,' but over the years I've seen a lot with my own eyes.

I think about my bed. I'll sleep, yes, I'll fly to another world. I'm so tired. Stress and strain all day long. I often feel that I'm walking a tightrope. A very tight one indeed. Yes.

I often say I've seen it all in this life, but daily life proves me wrong yet again. Today I went to a publisher, C., and made him an offer for a montage and printing.

'How is it you can give me such a low price?'

'I'm using a different method and so I'm saving a lot on the paper.'

'Well done, Chrysovalantis, you're brilliant! Why don't you nip off to Z.'s studio, where they're making a book for me, and tell them how to do it?'

I go, I tell them what to do, I waste two hours going back and forth and then I go back to C. to see what's going to happen with my offer.

'Leave it with me and I'll call you back tomorrow or the day after at the latest.'

Well, twelve days precisely have passed and not a squeak. I even left four messages with his secretary. I saved him all that money and he went elsewhere. I never imagined such deceit.

They're the same scribes and Pharisees who ten years ago applauded me and treated me like a hero, and when they didn't need me shouted, 'Crucify him, crucify him!'

I went to Mrs E., who is very kind and told me that she would certainly give me work. She's preparing a book. I trust her. I will also go to N. tomorrow. I didn't manage to today. I left a message with K. and I'm waiting for him to call. V. gives his jobs to a relation of his at the moment. We'll see.

I want to mention here that yesterday I kissed a Russian friend of mine at the bus stop—Claudia, who I hadn't seen for circa six months. It was just a kiss, nothing more. Besides, to be honest, I still haven't reached the point of sexual relations with a woman. With prostitutes, yes, but with women, no. I always look at them with caution. I lust, of course, but that's the limit. I think that the warm kiss of my friend has watered my garden.

> *I don't know what to do in life,*
> *Poor me, which road to take?*
> *My bird it sings no more,*
> *How will I find a girl*
> *In this sorry state?*

I wonder, are there boundaries to art? Particularly if it's daring? Just a question.

After Old Nick, I announced to everyone that I was looking for work. Two years went by, but to tell you the truth, what with my own problems and stuff at home, I didn't notice. There were many hours, of course, when I was overcome by the jitters and I grabbed the phone and called friends and acquaintances.

An old colleague said, 'Come here, Chrysovalantis, the company is in good shape and the boss is trustworthy.' I went, we had a chat, agreed on the salary and I began a month later. Then three other offers came in (a sudden winning streak after all that time), although I refused out of integrity. But I didn't settle down there, either.

I think that I made the best choice to go with my present company. The only downside: it's near a rubbish dump and far from home. Every morning I pay fifteen euros to get there by taxi. Thankfully a colleague takes me back in the afternoon.

Once, when I was about twenty-four, I designed a business card with telephone numbers, address, etc., and in an attempt to protect myself, under my name I wrote 'Black belt in karate'. When my father saw the mock-up, he started giving me stick.

'What's all this, have you gone mad?'

I waited for him to leave the shop and then I took it to the printer. 'Please, not a word to my father,' I said and paid him upfront.

As soon as he saw the money, he gave me a conspiratorial glance and replied, 'Whatever you say.'

Sexual thoughts have gripped me again. I think I have become a hedonist. Because of my diabetes. Since yesterday evening I've been thinking: how could Roro ever pay me back for all the money she squandered? If

I shagged her ninety times, would we be even? The question is how to invoice the service: street prostitute, hotel prostitute, red-light prostitute or escort? That needs some discussion. Yes.

I've taken a few blows in my time, so I tell myself to be a bit more realistic from here on. Why not write some TV series about my life, or better yet, about the women of my life? It would include only completely factual snapshots of my passionate life, without airbrushing, without interpretation, without intervention. That way, I'll bring to light the stones and arrows that were thrown against my pure heart. I will deliberately reveal the very bricks of the five-storey apartment block (each storey = a decade of my life) without the paint and plaster, without the oil paint, the primer and emulsion.

It will be simple, unembellished and unostentatious, therefore, like the monument to Athanasios Diakos in Alamana, so that everyone remembers that the Turks impaled him—and so they all (the Greeks to come and the young generations) remember to keep their heads high and their ideals, too. Fight for all you have! I've always loved my country—and women, and Europe, and Russia... I've been a good patriot.

I knew that at first I would be very busy and exhausted, but it doesn't bother me. (No idiot gives money for nothing.) I'm seriously worried until I manage to secure even a couple of clients, for starters—then I think that each will bring me others, as long as they find (as they always do) professionalism and consistency on my part, alongside passion and love for my work.

This afternoon at the Neon Café, I ordered yoghurt with whipped cream and truffle. The man at the buffet looked at me strangely. 'Do they go?' he asked. Well, so what if they don't go? It's like telling me that an icebreaker boat can't travel in a calm sea with no ice. The icebreaker goes everywhere; likewise, as we're poor, we should eat everything. The poor man wants two things: soul and vagina. I want everyone to remember that, always. Soul and vagina.

On Thursday I went to the doctor and got myself stitched up. I'm in great pain. The oral surgeon made local injections, cut my gums vertically, removed the roots of the teeth and then saw that there was a cavity full of pus. He cleaned it, and gave me stitches as it wouldn't close. The operation succeeded, thank God, but it tired me out. In the three hours that the process lasted, I felt like fifty Bulgarian women were tormenting my body and I couldn't ejaculate. The dentist charged me a hundred and fifty euros, since I'm an acquaintance.

Where can I begin, a Casanova like me? I want to talk firstly about feelings. I urgently need to find a good girl, to love her and be loved back. I don't mind if she isn't beautiful, I just want her to be around the house, and not the cinema. I've gone crazy, I don't know what to do. I don't want to remain celibate and unloved. Masturbation doesn't really become someone of my age. Not to mention it raises my blood sugar. I prefer English women because they're more down-to-earth, not like Russians, who go up and down like yo-yos. Penis after penis. Besides, my family would accept an English or a French woman, but never a Russian or a Ukrainian. All of them belong to the 'M' category: Megaeras, Medusas, Monsters.

> I say therefore to the unmarried and widows, it is good for them if they abide even as I. But if they cannot contain, let them marry: for it is better to marry than to burn.

The operation on my upper-right jaw gave me unbearable pain and I needed to take very strong pills. I became one with my bed. I overdid it, yes. But oh, the pain.

Let's see how the new job goes. It's relaxed now, but soon the difficulties will come, when people go on leave. However,

> *If you're in debt, you don't speak*
> *You just sing and laugh*
> *And if you get in some fix,*
> *You prance around in your tears.*

MAKIS TSITAS

For me, a poem is the broth of a chicken soup. It's an experience of the soul. I am sort of both mad and romantic—so my friends say. I'm one of those who goes with the heart, not the head. A kiss, a bit of breast, that's enough.

I don't belong to the class of those brazen fellows who grab the bird by the hair and drag them off to bed. I'm not that kind of guy. For a man to do that means that he has been through a lot when he was young and now he's getting it all out. They used to say that about the notorious monster C., that he was forever being punished by his teacher when he was young and that's why he became a rapist. Women want normal men, without problems, so that they themselves can torment them. They keep the other kind of men for times of need: they use them as pimps in financial and family disputes. As the English, the Swedes and the French say, 'You don't eat with your dagger but with your spoon.'

Eumorphia believes that, too: that her pussy is made of gold. Her bloke has money, so I heard, and she's got him under her thumb, but I'm sure that before she chucks him out she'll take his underwear off him.

There's no doubt now (though I found out after the party was over, unfortunately) that the woman in question has a depraved mind and believes in self-enrichment. These sorts of women will stop at nothing.

Today I was on a job on Zoodochou Pigis Street when I saw Old Nick. He was all lovey-dovey.

'Chrysovalantis! How are you? You look great, you old rascal!' Then he got out some advertising leaflets and gave them to me.

'Have you been networking? If you get me a lot of customers, you'll earn twenty percent of the profits. I'd love us two to work together again.'

'OK, I'll give you a call and we can chat.'

I threw all the leaflets into the first bin I came to.

As Akis Panou says,

Leave the madman to his madness and don't revive him,
You'll never really know what a madman has in mind.

Before Old Nick, I worked for M., who was a partner of L. They never started out earning a day's wage: they opened a good printers with modern machines straight away. There was a logical explanation for L., since he was from an old Athenian family (his father was a doctor, etc.), but not for M. Everyone said he was some freemason or mafioso, since he had admittedly suspicious contacts abroad.

Anyway, at some point when everything was going swimmingly and the company had managed very quickly to become the largest and most respected in the field and the relationship between the two partners was excellent, L. was found murdered. Of course, all fingers pointed at M. Who knows who ordered him to do it. The prosecutor took it on immediately, but the case was closed in a hurry. And, of course, the huge business fell entirely into the hands of Mr M.

We had a bastard of a boss, who messed us about. Once he went too far: since I didn't register my attendance properly, he came over and slapped me twice. He almost dislocated my jaw. When I returned home, I told my father and he was outraged. He came with me to the company the next day and asked to see M. urgently. M. initially hid, since my boss was a friend of his and he clearly wanted to cover for him, but when he saw my father's insistence, he gave word to send my father into his office. It was the two of them in the office: my father, fuming, and M., calm as Buddha—or rather, calm as V., who killed his lover (a literature scholar) and then coolly faced his family. Well, he nonchalantly turned to my father and said, 'How much money do you want?'

My father, obviously, blew his top. He took me and left.

'They beat us up and then want to bribe us to boot. If we were in the army, I'd send him straight to security. Go and find work elsewhere,' he said.

I was like a young virgin who had her virginity violently stolen by her evil boss against her will and can no longer appear with her white dress of chastity.

This exchange left a great mark on me, for I perceived that for someone to protect his business and his minions, he will brazenly trample over truth, objectivity, principles and ideas of innocence and honour. And it's all to make a quick buck. Unfortunately.

He also once said to his secretary, 'All of you are one sewer to me... shits' and I heard him but I didn't get the point.

How I screwed up with that Eumorphia! Even my sisters told me so. I behaved so idiotically: going to London for her, bringing her whatever she wanted, paying all the money in the world, and she never even said thank you once in return. There I was, chasing her around, begging her for one glance, one word with her —a jockey bowing down to his horse, and the horse trampling him and dragging him through the dirt. Then she would sit and mock me in the office with her friend Mopface. They would always be whispering behind my back and giggling. When at last I realised this, it almost drove me insane.

'Go to the sea and shout; get out all your anger,' my psychiatrist friend suggested. I didn't go—I refused to do anything. I didn't even take my pills. I didn't tell him that.

I've just remembered Eumorphia's sister, the notorious Katy. She was also a cunning thing. She was convinced, like her sister, that she would climb the ladder by being a whore. They had made a pact between them against me. I would call their home with an excuse to talk to Eumorphia, and she would deliberately make Katy pick up.

Once I called with the perfect excuse.

'Could I speak to Eumorphia, please?'

'She's not here,' said Katy, hesitantly.

(She knew who I was, and I knew who she was, but we played dumb.)

Since I realised, however, that she was there, listening, I carried out a test. 'Could you please let her know that I have her business cards ready?'

Eumorphia grabbed the receiver and said, 'Stop calling my home every five minutes. I'll see you tomorrow at work.'

Then I said to myself, 'How much of a whore is that woman, and how much more of a whore will she become…?' Not for a moment did she think of the pain and effort I had made to print thousands of cards for her on the sly, always in danger of Old Nick catching me and making a fool of me.

I want to excel in my field. I want to add something to the world of the book. Since I am active and emotional, I want to bring two people together to make love. Why not have such-and-such a publishing house make love to my company…? It's my pleasure, even if I can't take part: I'm satisfied just watching. Life, in any case, is only born from love-making. How else can a woman beget a child if the penis does not penetrate her private parts? With love, friendship and tenderness—not with savagery. The child born of rape may well become mad, as the Americans say; might well kill one of his parents.

A short while ago I saw a woman and it unsettled me. I had met her two months ago and fallen in love—but I realised that she was older than me. A stunner, of course. I like women who have that brown-blonde hair and I like the way they style it. I don't know what her job is. I'm embarrassed to ask. I don't want to open up—I've taken enough blows in my life. Anyway, I've been keeping my head down for a while. I'm afraid. I don't have the energy for more adventures. Her hands look like a cleaner's. I don't know. In the past, with that good-for-nothing Eumorphia, I didn't even know what degree she had, whereas she knew everything about me. Later I found out that she studied graphic design. I don't want to embolden the other person. If I asked her that sort of thing, she would think I was easy prey.

I'm beginning to like the new girl who makes the coffee at the Neon Café. She wears no earrings, keeps her hair in a bun and has nicely shaped eyebrows, too. She's got small bosoms and wonky lips. A woman should have straight, broad lips—pink is the best colour, but whatever colour they are, it should be the same as her nipples. Perhaps the 'lower lips', too—I haven't noticed. Christ, I'm going to Hell. I don't know why my mind continually turns to those things. I've wondered about this before. I'm afraid that my diabetes has really affected me. I don't like that at all. I want to be just, to have a clear conscience and a chaste life. That's the only way to God. Life is very short, fast paced—fast food and not a care in the world. We should care about the next life, about eternity; and personally, I need to love God as much as I can. I can only speak for myself. That's why they say that man is answerable to his soul. He can only make judgements about himself. Thus the Gospel says, 'Do not judge lest you be judged.' I want to go to Heaven. Is there anyone, however sinful he is, who wants to go to Hell? I think I'll be OK.

The opinion of others used to interest me a great deal. I admit it. I got that from my parents, unfortunately. I based my life on what others would say. It took my psychiatrist two years to get that out of my system. Now I'm not bothered at all about others' opinions. I have seen that my problems can't be solved by some Russian bird. I'm drowning; how can I save myself? By grabbing onto her bra? It'll snap immediately—or, even worse, she'll take it off herself and I will drown, and at the end of that she'll say, 'You keep the bra, I'm off.' Yes.

It's easy to go with a prostitute. The difficulty is hooking a proper woman on your line, catching her and reeling her in. As my friend says, too, 'Since the foreign women came, we've felt like men.' Correct, because Greek women spit on us; they are all highfalutin.

So, I left the drawing rooms and went to the shit, and found understanding there. The company is next to the sewer. The whole area smells like a cesspool. But then again, and I'm certain of this: it's my best option.

My father and mother used to go to the Officers' Club. One New Year's Eve, my grandmother came to take care of us because they were going to the ball. My father, with his uniform, sword, and Brilliantine in his hair, saluted us with gusto. Mother, her hair in a bun, wearing an off-the-shoulder ballgown, a pendant on her neck, satin gloves to her elbows, a lamé clutch and her fur, beamed at us like a queen. They left, all smiles and laughter. But they returned before midnight. Dad was irate, mum in tears. 'Did you argue again?' asked Grandma, and sent us to our rooms. Dad shouted, 'She trod on me in the first waltz, the idiot. She made a fool of me.'

'If you don't stop all the sentimentalism, Chrysovalantis, who will look out for you?' my doctor asked me. He meant women. Four or five men will fight your corner. But what whore will do that? You can't trust any of them. A woman in the home is absolutely fine: modest and subservient. But when she goes out, she immediately puts on a badge, like an athlete. He'll put on the shirt of his team, and she'll put on the badge of her whoredom. That's what happens.

My psychiatrist was director of the psychiatric clinic for ten years at a large army hospital with a serious epidemic of coloureds and natives. If you're a black man and you want to become an officer, they can't just put you into the group willy-nilly; the psychiatrist will have to check you over first. That's what happens in America. Even in the case of some crime having been committed, it's the psychiatrist that goes in first, then the investigator. They say that psychiatry is the most difficult branch of medicine because it is obliged to stop the damage before it happens. We don't have one mind, we have two: the right and the left, the good and the bad, the straight and the perverse. Balancing the psychoneurotic system is the task of the psychiatrist.

I believe that women disdain me because I can't get it up. They realise this—they see it straight away. All these pills hit my heart, eyes and dick. I'll do an ultrasound of the penile system to see which blood vessels have broken, making me permanently flaccid.

If a woman suggests we go to some hotel or to her flat, and I take off my pants, she'll say, 'You silly bugger, why have you let your dick go?'

How Old Nick, who had all the psychological problems in the world, had so much sex ('Once a day, certainly!') is a mystery. I want to ask my doctor, see what he says.

Now with my new job I feel I have fallen into safe hands and I will try by hook or by crook not to lose my position. That's why I am always obedient to my seniors. My boss has destined me for his forthcoming commercial sector.

'You're the most capable for the position,' he says.

Alongside me there will be, among others, his wife and daughter. I'm rather pleased that he has brought me into his family. I'm proud of myself.

Right, hear something unbelievable: that whore of whores, Mopface, called me to make some restaurant menus she wants for a place in Arta! After everything she's done to me, all her games at my expense, all the unscrupulous slander. The cheek! She called me, she said, to see how I was. How concerned for my health she was! I said nothing. When she saw I was avoiding her, she gave me Eu-bloody-morphia's news: she's had two children in three years. So, her bloke's working and she's sitting on her arse all day. That lady's got it sorted.

I always considered my mother and my sisters unique —living in a safe, bolted castle. All other women were an escape, but a paid escape. Perhaps that's why I never married.

The doctor told me that I have aged from my diabetes. But when I constantly try to please everyone; when I've been unemployed so long; when my body has been so exhausted; when I have been through so, so much, how can I expect to get it up? The doctors say they see twenty-five-year-old men—six-foot tall, handsome, thin as rakes—who can't get it up. It's down to the angiopathy that can occur in a young person and the pills he needs to take. There are sedatives for the mind, for the nerves, the blood vessels… like those which I take every morning and evening for my heart. The oral surgeon who operated on me was exasperated. 'You're on so many pills… how will the wounds close?' All the while I was thinking of the wounds I'd opened in my bank cards.

Yesterday evening I fell into great musing. Our lives aren't only sex, yet why do I always think about sex? It's a sin. There are so many other things that should come first: health, work, pulling myself together again. Sex will come later. I mean, I shouldn't try to buy a cage without having a bird. Find the canary first and then buy him the canary seed. That's how it's done.

I fell asleep with these thoughts and saw Marinaki in my dreams.

She had died and was dressed as a bride in her coffin, with long red nails and my bracelet on her left wrist. The procession set off towards the cemetery and we all followed in tears. From the megaphone on the hearse, which suddenly became a lorry, came the song, 'Sometimes Buddha, sometimes Kouda, sometimes Jesus, sometimes Judas,' and everyone, apart from me, began to sway. I looked at them, speechless. Then a samurai with a wooden leg came up to me and said, 'Come on, Chrysovalantis, she's calling you, she's missed you a lot,' and I woke up covered in sweat and choked up with tears.

They didn't even invite me to the embassy—I, who have taken them all out a dozen times! I found out that it's the reception for their national festival today, and they invited several Greeks but not me. When I have done so much for them! It turns out that Russians are utterly ungrateful. Well, a monk from Esfigmenou Monastery once told me, 'You give your hand to a Russian and he'll first kiss it, then lick it and then bite it off.'

I have sinned over the last days: I pick up a channel with pornos from the '80s, where blonde women strip naked on jeeps. I want to delete that channel but I can't—our television is very strange, it needs special settings and I'm afraid to change it in case I do some serious damage. But I need to get rid of it post-haste to stop sinning.

When I had no money, I had an awful time. I would often come back home from work on foot. Whole kilometres. If you have no money, people pretend they don't know you. You call the offices of people you thought were your friends and they tell their secretaries to say that the director is out. When you have money, you feel you have alternate options in your life.

You say, 'I could take a taxi and come home like a gentleman; I could eat in a good restaurant; I could help my father—doctors will rob you blind. Often when various women left me it was because they soon realised that I wasn't the moneybag they expected.

When someone knows you have money, he won't demean you. Ever.

I come now to my new love interest.

The way she talks makes me crazy—it's feminine, impulsive. It's like she's saying, 'Come on, I'm waiting for you.' I hope she's not one of those who looks a man in the pockets, not in the eyes.

I hope to become the most pleasing and unforgettable in her—limited, I would like to believe—experience. For the moment we're just talking; I'm treading gingerly. I don't think she's a megalomaniac. She seems down-to-earth and respectable. She's called Liza and she's the new secretary at work.

'Good morning, Chrysovalantis, how are you?' she says to me every morning. I interpret: 'Good morning, Chrysovalantis. Tie me up.'

Ah, would that a woman could love me at last!

I frequently buy lottery tickets, now that I have a bit of cash. Not so much to win as to hear the blessings of the seller. If you get blessings from a lottery ticket seller, you'll be happy. You need to get blessings from your mother, your parish priest and your lottery ticket seller.

Your mother, because she raised you with her blood and tears; your priest, who baptised you and took away your sins; and the lottery ticket seller, because he will bring money to your pocket.

If Eumorphia was with me, she wouldn't let me buy lottery tickets. She would grab the money I was taking out of my wallet and put it in her bag. That's the sort of whore we're talking about! God, forgive me. I'm swearing again, but what does a whore want? Sex and money. And Eumorphia is a certified whore.

Roro imagines herself differently, because her house is full of photographs of body-builders: framed, half-naked photos in all the rooms. A blatant sex fantasy.

I think that she was probably raped when she was little, and so she vowed to punish any good sort she came across.

I am convinced that her psychosis for every deviant, mad and filthy thing is bolstered by the internet. She must go on porn sites and steal ideas. Not to say that she wouldn't be capable of meeting people for a fee.

I also go on the internet, but for completely different reasons: to develop my network of colleagues in the publishing world. A new clientele—the so-called virgin clientele. Nonetheless, they're not guileless people, from whom I can just take money. It's a trustworthy clientele, serious and dignified.

The field of publishing is not as I knew it thirty years ago. In the sector of writers, translators and editors it has retained its high standards. But the production sector has gone: it has fallen into the hands of barbarians and pilferers. The hands of parachutists. I'll say it in my own words: we've reached the level of genetically modified print typographers.

Every time I go somewhere for coffee, I have my bag right beside me. If there are lots of people, I hug it to my chest, I clasp it with one hand and with the other I drink my coffee, looking around politely. There are so many foreigners walking among us; we hear about so many thefts every day. My sisters say to me, 'You're going too far'. And I respond, 'I'm being careful.' You never know when the evil hour will come. Yes.

It was belittling for Mopface that Eumorphia was so popular while she hadn't so much as seen a picture of a dick. I mean of a living one. She must have seen some painting or statue in a museum or gallery, yes, since as we know she loves the arts. To be true, she didn't have the debased nature of Eumorphia, at least regarding sex. Eumorphia would say outright, 'How much can you give me? What are you offering?' She was harsh and brazen. She seized F.'s car, and took whatever she could from me, likewise the biologist, and in the end she pounced on her current man, who certainly has property. It's out of the question that she would get chummy with a poor or financially average person. Of course, she squandered her grandmother's money, too. I think she would be capable of coming up to me in the street and saying, 'Thank God I found you! My mother's in hospital and they're asking for a thousand euros. Save me!' There's no way I would help. My doctor has stressed that repeatedly, and he's very strict about it: even if she's on fire, you won't bat an eyelid. Indifference and contempt! At heart he's telling me to become a stolid Englishman, not some fake Athenian—to remain a respectable lad, obeying my elders and those who wish me well.

Anyway, I have managed this twice. Once when the lady in question came to visit Old Nick's company, just before it closed, and I pretended I didn't see her, and once more when she called me because she wanted some information and asked to meet. I didn't say a word, neither 'yes' nor 'no', I just slammed down the receiver. The woman toured the whole of Europe and all the glamorous universities and at the end she came back to me. She needed my help again. She returned to her old haunts, but she found them deserted, and old shepherd Chrysovalantis, who she used to send to pasture her sheep (I pastured them; she got the milk), she found without his cape and shepherd's crook. Things change.

When my little sister goes out to the market alone I worry. I'm afraid something will happen to her. Some scoundrel will do her harm. That's why I often pick her up afterwards. I've had that anxiety from the moment she was born. At secondary school I would run off at every break-time to the primary school—which, thankfully, was nearby—hide behind a wall to see how she was, and as soon as I was sure she was OK, I would go back to class without ever telling anyone my concern. I always felt like her father.

My new boss gave me his office to reward me for the effort I've made at work. He also promised me that he would soon give me a raise. I'm working on business promotion. It's my pride and honour, since I will soon owe nothing to anyone in the business.

He is a true employer, not like Old Nick, whose only gift to me in eleven years was one book. Not to mention Givashit, who didn't even give me a piece of chewing gum (not so much as a sugar-free piece).

I'm very content with this job. And the money always arrives on time. I hope I can hold it down. I'm not concerned about the kudos but about earning the money that I owe. I need to be patient. Like a prostitute is patient in her work. She takes beatings, shaggings, violence, social disdain and oppression. Any old fellow goes along Zinonos Street and she has to find some way of turning him on. (She does all that and essentially earns nothing, because the pimp takes it from her.)

That's how Old Nick treated us—like whores. And we thanked him for it!

I took my family out yesterday to celebrate my new job. I told them to wear their best (after all, I've finally put on a suit again) and I took them to an aristocratic restaurant in Kefalari. We haven't done that for a long time. My parents don't really leave home these days, but they were delighted with my suggestion, not to say proud of their son. Everything was exceptional: the food, the wine, the service, the atmosphere. My pleasure to stand the steep bill. We had a wonderful time.

I'm looking for the next woman. Nonetheless, it is with pleasure that I note that the cost is going down: Eumorphia took a hell of a lot; Roro, quite a lot; Marinaki less; and the Ukrainian even less—thanks to the experience I am gradually obtaining. In total, fifteen women have been through my life. I think I know by now how to handle them.

I think that if Eumorphia and Roro decide to become rich, they'll easily manage it. The former could find a dozen idiot-victims like me. The latter, if she erected a lighthouse on a headland and made an announcement that, from this time to that, you can come to give her a shag, the boats would throng the place every day: row boats, fishing boats, cruise ships, all lining up. She would give them her coordinates. She wants to research male endurance. In depth.

I returned home late yesterday—I had a small, bar-shaped problem. Nothing came of it, but what with this and that, it was 2 am. When I opened the door, I saw my mother waiting for me.

'Why aren't you asleep, darling mother?'

'Now you're back, my boy, I'll go to bed.'

She's always done that, ever since I was a teenager. And I never understood how, despite her illness, she became completely lucid when she realised I was late in returning.

I have a secret dream: to sing at the National Opera; to give a solo recital in various musical genres.

'They only invite recognised artists there. How will you manage to perform?' my psychiatrist friend said to me when I confided in him.

I disagree. Besides recognised artists, I've seen a whole load of chancers and tone-deaf people. They must have political sway, from ministers upwards. So yes, how will I get in, innocent and honourable nightingale that I am? I'm afraid that I won't ever be able to cross the laurel-crowned gate of the Opera. That saddens me. Rather a lot.

I don't have many happy memories of childhood. Even when I went camping near Florina I didn't have a good time, because they made us work. From twelve to fifteen years old I went there in the summer for some peace and quiet, and they put me to work. The whole environment was military. I don't like excessive discipline, that's why when my father pressured me into going to military school I ran away.

At a book launch once I met a beautiful woman who introduced herself as a playwright. (Unfortunately she'd had nothing staged.) I approached her because I saw how delicately she ate the peanuts while holding her drink, with the poise of a ballerina.

The first time we went for coffee (at Zonars) I said to her sensually, 'I want to become the India ink in your fountain pen, with which you compose your modern, edifying, epic-lyric plays and monologues.' She said nothing—anyway, she was a sphinx-woman— but I saw that she liked it, even though I felt slightly awkward on her behalf. I lost her afterwards. I don't remember why. Twenty years have passed and I can still see the movement of her neck as she leant towards me to hear what I was saying.

I forgot to say that I went to a bar yesterday—to unwind. On Agiou Konstantinou Street. Outside were four pimps. One said,

'Do you want company for twenty euros?'

'OK.' I gave it to him and went in.

There was thick smoke and a strong smell, but as I had paid, I sat in a red velvet armchair. A girl with lovely breasts immediately came up to me and said, 'Will you buy me some champagne?'

I almost said yes, she had such lovely skin and eyes dark as coal. But champagne is expensive. What if she put something in it and I was robbed? I saw the man who took my twenty, in a corner sniggering. 'Chrysovalantis, they know you're fat and innocent. Beware. Beware!' I said to myself.

'Give me a minute to withdraw some money. You order,' I said and disappeared.

Will you tell me I had sly intentions? I just wanted a cuddle. But not champagne! The shame! Thus I escaped Scylla and Charybdis. The women I know are Scyllas. Those I don't are Charybdises.

I want to change career. I want to become a wine merchant. I have salesmen friends who used to be in printing and book-binding and now they sell mobile phones, electrical goods and wine, and they earn about six times as much. Working with wine seems easy and agreeable to me—you go to liquor shops, catering companies and public offices to sell.

When I was little I wanted to make money, turn it into gold sovereigns and go and buy a castle. That was my dream, and lithography would be a side hobby.

I have had some unforgettable times on Mt. Athos. I remember Father Pavlos at Simonopetra Monastery, who told me repeatedly what I needed to do. First, save my body—become thin through fasting and prayer— and then bless everyone and everything.

Those devout services—a divine thing! I was in a spiritual Hollywood. Of course, we're talking about something much more elevated: Elvis's voice cannot enchant you, however great your unrequited love is, whereas the melody that comes from the heart of a monk is incense bringing joy to the soul. The tender notes from the pure monkish larynx are like those of a baroque opera choir at the Scala in Milan, or of an American overproduction of a religious musical.

A compliment from a woman can send a man to the moon. Or to Heaven. That's why I have occasionally pursued beautiful girls, with the idea that they will help me psychologically in losing weight. None of them did. I chose beautiful ones because I believed that I would also become beautiful. I'm not egotistical, but I hoped to find a beautiful companion to live with, and everyone would say, 'Look at him, what a beautiful wife he found!' A huge risk. I've come a cropper. I think, however, that I deserve a better future, and that I will manage to live as I dreamed when I was young, in a spiritual princedom inside my castle.

My boss knows that although Old Nick went bust, he had an exceptional client base, and he asked me to bring him in to collaborate. There I am, pretending I've seen the back of him. Why would I want to give myself that nuisance again? I'm bathed in sweat just thinking about it. Knowing how erratic he is, I think he's even capable of closing our company. Then I'd be running around looking for work again. Better to leave it.

Diabetes affects the penis. It's well known. The same goes for excessive smoking and coffee. I mean, you can see a naked girl and feel desire, but the erection won't be there. Thankfully I still have wet dreams. That means that my organism is working regularly. The balls are still balls, blood is circulating, but there is no erection. I will try to find an andrologist. Post-haste. I must.

I wonder, if I go on a TV channel, could I direct a conversation, could I conduct an interview or would I be too awkward?

Unfortunately, I don't have the appropriate educational background. And my jaw slips out of place a bit—I don't quite talk correctly. This began exactly ten years ago, when I developed a palsy. It was like a mini-stroke. The doctors said it was from the cold. Some sensitive blood vessels were affected and my mouth went wonky—it recovered somewhat with cortisone injections. Now with the diabetes, I admit that sometimes my tongue trips up a bit, too. I'm taking pills and sometimes I'm OK. But 's' comes out as 'th' (not always) and 'r' (always) 'rrro'. Yes and sometimes I dribble a bit, OK. That's why I wonder: could I be in front of the camera?

A strange thing: when I sing, I am absolutely fine. But you couldn't sing the news, could you...?

It would be of great interest to me to write articles on subjects to do with work and the financial protections of workers. That is a serious matter—financial protections of workers, who are simultaneously consumers. I've read up on this, I've taken notes. I've looked a lot into this whole business.

The goal of both my big and little sister is now plain: whatever I earn, I put on the table for them. That's the truth. Therefore, I need to keep a certain distance from the situation. I think that I shouldn't mention my finances any more—they shouldn't know what I'm doing, who I'm working with. They shouldn't know anything. I need to protect myself to some extent.

Today I went to a publisher, a new client, and she asked me about Old Nick: 'What's your opinion?'

'A good person, but he went bust.'

I didn't know if she was doing that to sound me out—his ghost follows me everywhere and after all these years I need to defend myself.

'A good person? He squandered everyone's money, and we're left with IOUs in hand!'

'Well, yes, he also owes me some compensation,' I murmured, so she would pity me and place an order with me. I couldn't face going back to my new boss empty handed.

I think about Marinaki a lot. Every minute of the day. I regret that I lost her, but I didn't have the money to keep her. What should I do, throw my own family out into the road?

If my finances take an upward turn, I'll look for a Swedish woman, so she has some culture. I don't like the behaviour of Greek women who only care about lipstick, phones and nice cars. I want my woman to feel a bit like a villager, yes, but a cultured one. She should like home life and not be slipping out willy-nilly.

On the one hand you have Marinaki, and on the other, all other women. Let's say it plain: no one can eradicate my love for that girl.

My mother deteriorated a lot after the birth of my little sister. After six months my father asked for a transfer to Larisa and he left us behind. Initially, Mother would call him, plead with him, remonstrate, but in time she accepted it. Her face turned expressionless, her eyes distant. She would sit all day on the sofa looking at the floor. My big sister and I took on the household chores: she shopped and cooked, I changed the little one, fed her, put her to bed. Grandma would come with aunt Dionysia every Saturday to do the cleaning and ironing. We would hear them cursing my father, saying he deliberately didn't come back, that he led his own life and sent money, as if he were divorced.

When, after two years, he deigned to visit, he realised at once what was happening. One afternoon
when he came back from the café, he saw Mother sitting motionless on the sofa and the two of us doing the
chores. He shouted, 'What are you doing, you useless
thing? Is that how a mother behaves? Or a wife and
partner?' He grabbed her by the scruff of the neck and
slammed her head against the wall. My mother didn't
show any resistance, she didn't squeak—as if it didn't
hurt, as if she didn't feel it. My big sister hugged me
and I held the baby. I almost crushed her from fear.
Thankfully my grandmother intervened just in time.
Otherwise he might have killed her. After that, Aunt
Dionysia took the three of us to her house for a long
time.

I was exhausted today. I went to five meetings to arrange work. I was constantly going to and fro. In my
opinion, I made them some pretty interesting propos-
als, but I don't know if I convinced them. We'll see. It's
a high-pressure job: both my employer and his daughter are constantly breathing down my neck, demand-
ing me to bring in clients. They pressure and browbeat
me, but I'm being strong and I think I can withstand it.
I withstood Old Nick all those years.

I think that the person who collects money owed
has the most difficult job. After that, the salesman. If
I can consolidate myself into this double-position, all
the companies will want me and they'll give me good

pay. I will be a good, capable and well-versed worker in this tough but worthwhile profession. Perhaps it is the most worthwhile in the world—and I don't think I'm exaggerating. Einstein will be forgotten, you see, and Van Gogh will be forgotten, but Gutenberg—never.

Dark thoughts have taken hold of my mind and soul. Recently, yet again, I haven't been able to get it up. My diabetes is to blame. It affects testosterone. My doctor told me. I went to see him yesterday in a panic. He told me to do a triplex of my penile blood vessels, but I am embarrassed because my little chap has shrunk a great deal. I'm embarrassed in front of the nurse who'll see it and think it's non-existent. I think, therefore, I should begin to sleep like the Chinese, facedown and naked with my dick between the slats of the bed, lengthening from the weight. It would hasten the whole thing along, make it bigger, then I would go. Up until two years ago, you see, I was hard as nails. Now it's gone right down and I'm terribly embarrassed. Women re-alise that. They say, 'There's no way that bloke can do the deed', and they start playing psychological games with you. She sees that you're no Lothario, nor are you trying any cheap tricks on her when you're together. Ergo, you're embarrassed to show it to her. That's when the whorish stuff begins.

An example. Claudia, the Ukrainian, had her bloke with her when she invited me to her home. We were sitting in the living room—the two of us on the sofa and him in the armchair—talking about this and that, eating a custard pie with kaymaki ice cream that I had bought. At some point, he got up and went to the kitchen. Then she shuffled closer to me, almost gluing herself onto me. 'Look at what my girlfriends have written to me,' she said, getting out her phone.

'Shift over a little, so he doesn't come back in and we get in trouble,' I said.

She stroked my leg, smiling. I realised at that moment that he was in on the game of taking my money. I was giving her pocket money on a daily basis. How did I, a connoisseur of women, end up in that situation? What can I say...? She implemented some cunning tricks. She showed indisputably that she was a master of the genre.

I'm saying all this now so I don't say it to my psychiatrist and he immediately throws pills at me. If I tell him gently, he will give me weaker ones, and fewer of them. I know.

A truthful word costs nothing, a deceitful one costs a lot. Lying, I conclude, is dear. Ultimately there is no justification for it. That was the mistake of my old employer, Old Nick, who believed that his lies would bring all good things to the company. He committed a whole load of idiocies and made everyone suffer on his account. The consequence of lying is loss of trust. I've learned that.

The Devil is the father of deceit. That's what the Holy Scriptures say. God doesn't condone lying.

Lying, particularly in the professional sector, spells disaster. My boss over at the rubbish dump said to me some time ago, 'Bring you publisher friends here so we can get some work.'

I brought him a load of my own clients, and then the crafty bugger, even though we had given low prices verbally, charged whatever he wanted on the invoices.

I said to myself, 'Chrysovalantis, what's going on, are you going to let this opportunist destroy the name you've built up in the publishing world for so long with your blood and sweat?' OK, you'll ask me, what do I expect from a mad-keen gambler, frequenter of casinos and racing? Solvency and consistency? I was compelled, therefore, to write this:

> *What do I want with the drawing rooms*
> *So choc-a-bloc with frauds?*
> *On the white sheets*
> *Lie wounded jaws*
> *Blood is running and saliva, too:*
> *All the rich are worse than whores.*

I brought them a trustworthy client, my friend Mr S., who had a good job for us, a calendar in a run of ten thousand copies, which he wanted urgently for a shipping company. It was the tenth of the month and the fellow said he wanted them in twenty days, i.e., on the thirtieth. I asked my boss and he agreed. The twelfth of the next month came around, then the twentieth, and the calendars still hadn't been delivered. Every day Mr S. called me and said, 'What's going on, Chrysovalantis?'

On the twenty-eighth I went to my boss, 'What's happened? The customer is all fire and fury!'

What did the idiot respond? 'Well, why hasn't he told us all this time that his work was urgent?'

What can you say to that?! You swear inside (God forgive me) and you prepare your bags.

Not to mention that the boss's daughter turned out to be very cunning. (I'll curse women again and they'll say that I'm prejudiced). To my face she was all sweetness and light: 'Chrysovalantis, please, Chrysovalantis, thank you,' but behind my back she laid into me—both to the other personnel but also, unfortunately, to our clients. I was compelled to leave. I have my dignity, my prior experience. I'll find a better job.

I've thought seriously about it. It would be better to marry a chaste English woman, have my job, my family, comfort and holidays in the country. At heart I'm a very conservative, frugal person. I've been wearing the same shoes for a year and a half. Life goes on, both for us poor and for the rich. 'The rich have wanted, and have suffered hunger: but they that seek the Lord shall not be deprived of any good.'

Then there was the situation with my father. He fainted out of the blue. When he came round he had serious dizziness. The ambulance came and took him to Evangelismos Hospital. They kept him there for a week to examine him. I was both looking after my father and my boss was at my throat. I had informed him, of course, but when someone doesn't want to pay you, he finds an excuse.

Employers want employees to be infantrymen, but what about their dignity? The week I went back to work, he shouted at me. I was furious. I went into his office and slammed the envelope with my orders onto the table. I was taking orders on the phone every day I was with my father. When he realised how much he had insulted me, he began to grovel, saying how worried he had been about me and that sort of rubbish. But the deed was done: he had shouted, 'Are your sisters and mother so useless that you have to stay at the hospital yourself?'

For me, it's family first and me second. If you take away my spiritual peace, what good is all the praise? You have to accept your colleague, especially in the difficult hour. How could I accept him and his company, so far away from my home, when I was paying fifteen euros each morning for the taxi out of my own pocket, even though they had promised to pay my travel? And it was literally in a shithole. All too recently another drawback emerged: right next to the company, the Municipality of Kifisia then built its rubbish dump. So, shit on one side, rubbish on the other. That came and finished the whole thing off. Thank God I cut and run.

Ah, my heart sighed and I wrote a verse.

I, a poor, beleaguered monk in this life, my face covered in spiritual stains from hardship I have suffered from my fellow man, I say to myself,

> *Learn to live humbly,*
> *Learn to live stupidly*
> *And those who pretend to love you*
> *Learn that they hate you.*
> *For that's the truth.*

Interpretation: learn to live without romantic love, travel, money. Play the idiot so no one approaches you. Those who pretended to love you, well, at heart they hated you. That's the conclusion. It's not a momentary inference.

I make all my calls looking for work outside the house, so I don't upset my family. I still haven't found the courage to tell them that at fifty-one I am unemployed again.

'Good morning, I would like to speak to the director of your company, please. My name is Chrysovalantis C., I am a lithographer with twenty years' experience. I would like to send you my CV and arrange a meeting with you.'

'We'll be in touch,' they always reply. It's like all the secretaries have swallowed the same tape.

It's a farce. Despite that, I continue every day to do personal promotion. I know that to find work in our day and age you need to bleed. Every day without interruption, from morning until four o'clock, I run around handing out CVs, meeting people, talking. Around five I become tired (from the diabetes), and I go home. My family think I have returned home from work. I eat little, sleep and go out again. If I stay at home, I will start crying and they'll catch on.

In the end, I couldn't take it. I went to my friend Sarantos, who works for a large printers, and I said, 'I want to speak to your boss. Make an appointment for me and tell him that I'm experienced. He shouldn't worry, I'm not the grasping type. I'm a very respected lithographer. I have a large clientele of publishers. Just say, "Go into the breach and fight," and you'll see what I can do for you.'

Unfortunately (I'm ashamed to say), Old Nick had previously brainwashed me into being his disciple. 'Chase them up so we get the work,' or 'Give them a higher offer, they've got money,' he would say and I would do it. I've changed now. I look at the client like a future employer. Besides, isn't that what many did in Old Nick's company? Haven't they now found work?

Look at Mopface, Eumorphia and Zoe,
Yiota, Sophia, Dino and Sotiri,
And here I am with no work, no bread,
No food, and an empty glass.
No one ever gave me a chance.

(I'm feeling inspired again today).

At present I'm waking up around seven. Thanks to the Furies, thanks to the debts I have at the banks. I get up, wash and shave quickly. My father watches television. He doesn't talk, but I know that he is depressed about my state. I have a coffee, make a sandwich, get my bag and leave. I take my diary with me and the *Directory of the Graphic Arts*—a doorstop of a book listing all the companies in the field. It's the only thing I managed to squeeze from Old Nick. All the rest were scattered to the four winds—phone numbers, useful notes, magazines, books, drafts. One day I went to the company to retrieve them, but it was all boarded up. Absolutely nothing was left after the sequestration. They took the lot. I don't want to remember it, as I get frustrated; it destroys my mood and my blood sugar goes up.

One Sunday, my family went for a swim at Schinias Beach. My big sister was fifteen, I was eleven and the little one was five. Indescribable joy. The sun was beating down and the beach was full of people. Dad helped us settle down. He swam and then went for a beer at the refreshment stand. We threw off our clothes and ran hand in hand into the sea. Mum, who up until then was unconcerned, was sitting fully-clothed on her towel. When she saw us go into the water, she began shouting in terror, 'Don't go in, you'll drown! Don't go in, you'll drown! Don't go in, you'll drown!' I realised then that my mother didn't know how old we were.

If two women engage in coitus together, it's abnormal. I've never seen two lesbians having sex, but I think that it is completely contrary to nature. It's worse than two men. With a man, OK, he turned into a queer. But a lesbian, what's she after? Her partner doesn't possess a member. So copulation per se cannot occur. This is what our Church calls 'female coitus': double feminine masturbation—two bodies whose orifices cannot exchange fluids.

When I worked for P., we printed a magazine in which all the photographs were of North-European lesbian-leaning ladies. That establishment was nothing but a brothel, since it only printed that kind of hard-core porno stuff. It was far out of town and the companies that publish that material would send their jobs there for printing and binding, out of the way. N. on Alexandras Avenue was one of their important clients. Apart from his well-known magazines (television, lifestyle and cooking), he also published that sort of thing.

Some time ago, I made a map with all the brothels of Athens on it, so I could easily locate them. I would lose my way, you see, distracted by my guilt.

Until I was thirty-six or thirty-eight I would go twice a week—I was working, I had money to play with. My diabetes hadn't crippled me then, of course, nor the debilitating palsy.

Why do I think about that now and constantly sin? I'm afraid I'm being tempted, and I will relapse into the same old things.

> Glory to you, King, God Almighty, who through your divine and loving providence have consented that I, an unworthy sinner, should rise from sleep and obtain entrance into your holy house. Accept, Lord, the voice of my prayer as you accept those of your holy and spiritual powers. And that not through my defiled lips, but from a pure heart and humble spirit may praise be offered to you.

'If you're going to wed some girl who'll make your life Hell, it's better not to get married,' my good confessor said to me.

'At fifty-one? Can I really get married now, Father?'

Seriously, I'm not thinking about it anymore. In any case I have the problem with my erection, so I'll end up cuckolded. That's the only certainty. Unless, of course, I move permanently to England or I find a tall, frosty Swede. Greek women are intolerant of big-boned people like me. (And as we know, Russian women are not for the home.)

I've been disillusioned by people's attitudes. But I'm not afraid of loneliness. When I grow old, I'll have a friend to support me, along with my little sister, my family and a good working environment. That is indispensable—to recover my self-worth. Work was a way of life for me. People like me never retire. I'll work all day and eat out, not at home.

Since my big sister broke her leg, the little one does the cooking every day, but I don't like eating at home at all. I do so because I'm penniless. In my personal life I want work, restaurants and quiet. I would like to go home only to sleep. I don't really feel like it's mine: perhaps because I didn't enjoy myself there when I was a child. Bad experiences. Just thinking about it upsets me and raises my blood pressure. Perhaps ultimately the most fitting title of my autobiography would be, 'Memories of an Unhappy Life'.

When I was young I would see the dump-trucks coming into the neighbourhood and emptying their gravel. I wanted one for myself. Once, Mother gave me my little sister's pram so I could take her for a walk. I went to the top of the hill and pushed the pram down. I gazed happily at it tumbling down, until it somersaulted and the little one was catapulted out. I hadn't thought that she might hurt herself. When I heard her screaming, I ran over, hugged her and gave her sweets that I always had in my pockets. But then my father appeared, who had watched the scene from afar. He was beside himself and gave me a serious thrashing.

I had other bad experiences, such as when I was working in the Church printers. We were in financial difficulties, with Grandma bedridden, so I had to go out to work. I've already said that priests are the harshest employers. They gave me a plate of food and a couple of coins. I was like a slave to them, always doing the worst jobs. A priest would shout at me every five minutes and give me a slap. I don't know why he did that. I conjecture that sadistic inclinations possessed him. Yes.

The woman knows that she has the upper hand. The man can only copulate with her if she wants it. She exploits that.

As a friend of mine told me (a notorious Athenian womaniser), the greatest compliment you can pay a woman is to tell her how beautiful she is. How exquisite everything about her is. Then there's no need for bracelets or books or mobile phones. Nor, of course, double beds, like I bought for Roro. She never even did me the honour of inviting me onto it. Roro was from the school of 'Eat here, spend there...' I was late in picking up on that.

Claudia would say, 'I love you so much' and suchlike, and, 'I can't pay my rent, what am I to do? Please find

me a job.' I was duty-bound, so I found her something
in a good bookbinder's.

I said to the owner, who I had known for many
years, 'Please treat her well.' I was at her side for whatever she wanted—like a father. But right from the start
she said, 'My bloke is so tender, my bloke loves me so
much,' and this and that. I thought she was talking
about that bruiser I had met that day at her home with
the custard pie, but ultimately, I found out from trustworthy sources that it was someone else: fifty-some-
thing, married with two grown-up children. I said to
her, 'Listen, sweetheart, I'm a child of the Church and
I know that it's a great sin to live with a married man
when he hasn't split up with his wife.' But she was indifferent. The same goes for him, who was also perpetrat-
ing a great sin, having left his wife to live with a
mistress. The lady, therefore, had two blokes wrapped
into one. And I reckon that she had both of them at
home at the same time (the Hotel Belle Ukraine). That's
probably why she had a narrow bed, like a sofa. It's well
known that orgies happen on narrow beds: in combina-
tion with a soft, comfortable mattress placed on the
floor. That explains why she would always come to our
dates exhausted and could hardly stay on her feet.

I confess that I still haven't understood the tactics
with which these foreign women make a laughing stock
of sensitive men who want to offer a little kindness.

She wanted—I'm certain—to marry the married
one (he was Ukrainian, too) and keep me as a financial

wild card. I still haven't understood what role I can play in a social circle with beautiful women. I also don't understand why they all think I'm the thyme bush from which they'll gather pollen. Under the rules of the Church, that's not on: to have the other chap as your bodily lover and me as your social lover. As my old confessor would say, 'Beware the Russian and Ukrainian women don't fleece you.' I misconstrued what he was saying, argued with him and didn't see him again.

My new confessor told me, 'When you hear her voice, just put the telephone down,' while my friend D. insisted, 'Get away from her as soon as possible and you'll see her opinion of you rise. She'll start chasing you. That's how you'll get your revenge.' He didn't have the best opinion of women from the Eastern Bloc. He thought they left their country either to take, or for tourism or for a better social life.

Madame Claudia invited me to her thirtieth birthday celebrations. Various men and women were there. A Ukrainian affair. I was the only Greek. To be honest, I actually had quite a good time because all the women, married or not, cast their nets at me. I was sitting, glass in hand, looking at the thong under the miniskirt of the one opposite me, while chatting with the one next to me. Their men were giving me dirty looks, but didn't say a word, simply because I was a local and they were scared. When I got home I realised that the pockets of my jacket were full of phone numbers. Once upon a time they looked at me, but it's too late now. I'm ill and penniless.

Some time ago my father was sick with jaundice and had stomach problems. I think that was when his friends started squandering his money—loans they wouldn't pay back. I never imagined that my family would fall into decline. I remember what my father went through to earn his living following his unjust discharge—and then some rotten priests (sadly they exist, too) told him that they needed money to publish books and do good deeds, and he gave to them continually. When he decided to put the brakes on, they threatened him with excommunication and he was terrified.

Despite his illnesses, he drank. Drinking is self-inflicted. (So, too, are laziness, loans and masturbation).

Claudia won't even get one euro from me. Let her get a job. I must admit that I was taken in at first. I couldn't imagine that the soft-spoken, polite Ukrainian girl would be so unscrupulous. Some time ago, I met a Russian woman in the same mould, but she reeked of it from the get-go. When I showed her photograph to my confessor, he went pale and said nothing, but I understood.

I was very worried about my father's health, and my mother's and sister's. Claudia thought that I would fall for her succours, and she offered to wash my clothes. I admit that moved me a lot, even though she never did it.

I never saw her naked. To get away from me, when I tried to move things along she said, 'The way you're touching me reminds me of when I was raped twice in Ukraine.' According to my doctor, that wasn't true. How was I pressuring you, madame, when I didn't even touch your breast or kiss your lips?

One day she came to me all beaten up, with a black eye and a big bruise on her right arm and another on her midriff. She must have been belted and kicked repeatedly. When I asked her what happened, she started making things up.

'Give me his number and I'll talk to him! If he touches you again, he'll have me to deal with.'

'No, no...'

'But don't you understand? Anyone who sees you now will think it was me that beat you.'

'Why on earth would they think that? What are you to me?'

After that I backed off.

Now she's after me. She sends me messages continuously on my mobile asking to meet up and have a chat. I want to distance myself now. I don't fancy being the tool of some wallet-snatcher. That's what I was to her: her fox terrier. Every evening that bloke would cook for me at her house—so they could milk me. And I would go and enjoy myself. You'll say, 'Didn't it bother you that she was with someone else?' Well, no, I got used to it. By the way, he was a classic case of BFII (Brute Force, Immense Ignorance). He played the good Christian, but I didn't once see him in the Russian church. Plus, he failed to notice that he ate four fried eggs with bacon and sausages on Good Friday. To cap it all, he had begun doing yoga, which, as we know, belongs to the field of parapsychology. A Satanic business.

What would I do with friends like that? Not to mention that she once said to me, 'You're cursing the person who puts food on your table just because he gives me the occasional slap.'

There's no doubt: those from the Eastern Bloc are not right in the head.

I need a serious woman to get along well with. And if she wants to massage my belly, or a little further down, so much the better. Otherwise she can stay away.

I heard that T., one-time legal adviser to Old Nick's company, put his mother in an old people's home. I consider that despicable, undignified and cowardly. A helpless widow, who had sweat blood to bring him up and educate him…

Every time I leave home, I'm afraid something will happen to my family or that the police will beat me up. That's why I always make sure I'm impeccably turned-out, and wearing my cologne, so that I won't be approached by any old rascal.

Until recently my little sister lived like a nun. She was always at home, doing chores, cooking, only watching the news and documentaries on television, taking her pills (for her stroke), going to church and to the Cathedral's nursing home. Aside from religious books, she was also studying at Panteion University. Unfortunately, it doesn't look like she'll be getting her degree. Her hair was always up when she went out, with her grey suit on and skirt below the knee. No make-up, nothing.

One evening, though, she came home with her hair cut short and dyed red, a tight T-shirt, trousers, heels. I despaired.

'What's all this? Have you gone mad? We're people of the Church.'

'Give me a break. Let me live my life.'

'So up until now, when you were a model girl, you weren't living your life?'

'Your confessor has brainwashed you,' she spat and left.

Since then, my big sister, who was in earshot, bangs on about it whenever she wants to put me in a difficult position. Lies, through and through. Both of them railed to friends and relatives about me. I found out all about it.

'Chrysovalantis is a tyrant, he torments us, he's destroyed our youth,' and a lot more disgusting and terrible things besides.

Then some cunning banker trapped them into acquiring credit cards, so they completely ignored me and took an abrupt turn in their lives. All day they went shopping and filled up their wardrobes.

I was still working then and I hadn't realised what was going on. They pulled this trick when I'd left the rubbish dump—again without compensation, and with my cards maxed (it had all gone on those sluts Eumorphia and Roro). I owed money everywhere, and my sisters couldn't give me the slightest helping hand. I am afraid that they also have debts at the banks.

Well, I gave in to all these things, but when I discovered about the policeman, I was incensed. I secretly turned on my little sister's phone and found many numbers, just initials and a lot of taxi drivers: 'Nikos Taxi', 'Yannis Taxi', 'Sifounas Taxi'. She had another number which read 'Café'. I called, withholding my number. It was an internet café in Vyronas. So, that was her haunt. I went and had a look. Darkened windows all over, and outside a poster of a naked woman, tinted purple, with her breasts out for all and sundry. I went in. There was a barely-discernible bruiser in the back, a black fellow from the United States. I sat for half an hour. Not a soul came in. Either they were money launderers or they were pimps or had a whorehouse inside—no doubt about it. The black chap and the waitress looked at me rather strangely. I was wearing dark glasses, a trench coat and a hat, in case my sister was in there. I had a coffee and as I left I asked for a card. They didn't give me one. They said they'd run out, even though there was a pile at the edge of the bar. I was certain that my sister frequented that place not just with the cop but with other studs.

Now she's at home and doesn't go out. At some point she realised that I was following her. She must have got wind of it, or was warned.

I asked her how she met the cop but she didn't tell me. It must have been when that confusion with the bank had arisen and we weren't receiving my bedridden father's pension. Two cops came in a police car to verify his signature, and they offered her a lift to the bank. The fellow in question probably made eyes at her in the police car—he would have realised right away how innocent and inexperienced she was. Maybe he said to her, 'Give me your number; you'll need documents like this all the time because of your father's condition. Here, take mine, too, and whatever you need, I'm here.' It's well known how cunningly these arch-pimps and night-time 'protectors' approach women. She accepted, of course. In good faith.

I have a friend at the Bank of Greece. Our friendship is an oasis. He's from an aristocratic Athenian family. For the roughly fifteen years I have known him, I've been going to his office at least once a week, all year round.

'Good morning, Mr Nikolaou, my good sir,' I say.

'Good morning, Chrysovalantis,' he replies.

'How are we today?'

'Fine, thanks. You?'

'In good health, thank God. Well, bon travail.'

'You too, mate.'

That's enough for me. It's not the quantity but the quality. That's our conversation every time. Nothing more and nothing less. Sincerity between the poor and the super-rich. I'm poor—I don't look like a freemason. Perhaps I am and don't know it? I wonder. Could they have made me one without my knowing? I don't know. I won't sell my faith for any financial dealings.

Two enormous bills have come in. The landline is three hundred and fifty euros and my little sister's mobile is five hundred. She's started disappearing again for hours with no explanation and coming home dishevelled.

I snatched her phone again at six in the morning when she was out for the count: she'd come back at dawn! I read all their messages to see what was going on between them.

She'd written, 'I'm yours. Completely.' I read it and almost got the palsy again. It's likely all those pills she's taking have raised her desires, and he's doing various deviant things to compromise her. I don't know. I'm scared. I'm terrified that he's blackmailing her. Perhaps he's saying, 'Give me money or I'll spill everything to your family and friends at the cathedral.' I hope I'm wrong. That fellow seriously needs to be banished from the Greek Police.

There's no way she'll find it where I've hidden it. She looked and looked but found nothing. She called me twenty times from eight o'clock in the morning until four o'clock in the afternoon, when she thought I was working. She shouted at me to give it back.

'Sweetie, you must have dropped it somewhere. I don't have it.'

She's always asking for money. Therefore, he's running through her disability allowance. She can't escape now. You mustn't fall into the honey bucket—you can't get unstuck. That happened to me, too. He might threaten to tell us all in every last detail. He's taken her virginity, and her poor little heart is trembling.

Anyway, she can't be madly in love with him. In a recent message he said, 'Come over. Even just for a kiss,' and she replied, 'I'm snowed under. I've got exams.'

I think that the cop, in order to draw her close again, must have promised her that he would find her work. That's why she declared proudly, 'I'm soon going to be working in television.'

'What do you mean? What'll you be doing?' I asked. She gave me an enigmatic smile.

'They want me on a morning show... they're after my expertise on religious matters.'

Our parents didn't react, of course—in the state they're in, with all the pills they're taking. My big sister shouted, 'Hold your horses, you're not going anywhere!'

'You'll do your head in,' said Aunt Dionysia, who came to the family council, as ever.

I didn't say a word. I was preoccupied by some little jobs I had here and there to earn some petty cash.

A good friend, whose advice I sought, said, 'Give her her phone back... After all, you don't know what their relationship is like... If the cop fancies her, he'll have already got her another...'

'I'm trying to protect her without hurting her. She's an inexperienced girl, sixty-seven percent disabled, and he's a married man with two children.'

'Chrysovalantis, sorry to say this, but at forty-five she's not inexperienced...'

At heart it's not their affair that bothers me, but their massive expenses. They won't stop thinking that whatever happens, I will get the whole family off the hook. I can't anymore. Enough is enough.

'Imagine we get phone bills again of over fifty or sixty euros...' I said to my friend. He knows that I'm not having him on.

'Look, if it's the landline, you'll all chip in. If it's her mobile, then her bloke can take the hit.'

'They need to start caring for Dad... They've been gobbling up half his pension all these years, and they get their Officer's Daughters' Allowance. Now they really need to look after him. I can't. Hospital bills, illness, unemployment—enough is enough. Only my big sister earns proper money, but she keeps it for herself. If I manage to throw in a couple of hundred euros, I'll feel better. The first month after the rubbish dump I didn't earn anything. Thankfully, I'm getting something now, but with huge effort. Little jobs, pocket money—and even that at a push.'

My sickness doesn't help—but I didn't say that to my friend. I don't want anyone to pity me. I have my dignity.

I know that my little sister is waiting for a suitable opportunity to make her next escape.

'I'll be like great Poseidon, brandishing his trident to strike down evil, and never, never tiring. I'll take my satchel, I'll pay people and I'll always have your back,' I told her when she was feeling better again.

She started crying. 'You don't own me. I have a personal life. Let me live it.'

I'm suspicious, I admit. My previous detective work taught me a lot. I know what people are capable of for a lay.

This interview was another washout. When will I find a proper job? This hand-to-mouth stuff isn't a solution. I'm in despair. How will I help my sisters get out of debt? I despair. Was my premature withdrawal from the company on the rubbish dump foolish? Should I be patient until I find a better job? I don't know.

My dream was to become a clergyman—an archimandrite and, by the grace of God, a metropolitan in the place of my birth, Karditsa. I would chant and infuse my life with music. That's why I go to the Russian Church: they let me be a subsidiary cantor.

Same old. My little sister came to me: 'I need money.'

I gave it to her, but I realised that she didn't want it for her credit cards. I smelled a rat. 'Chrysovalantis,' I said, 'Something's up. Here we go again.' Recently she's started going out again, almost every day.

I returned with my feet swollen from walking. She burst in, brash and indifferent. Just looking at her gave me heart failure—sexy clothing, make-up, red lips, hair puffed up. I was in shock.

'I'll be back in a couple of hours.'

'Where are you going at this time of night?'

'I've got things to do.'

Well, I took my pills and called her right away. She was at the doctor, the same one that looks after our parents. Five minutes later I was there in the waiting room.

She looked at me furiously. 'What are you doing here?'

'Aren't you ashamed to go around like a whore? What business does a girl who's had two strokes have creeping around the streets? I know that you've got a date after the doctor. That's why you're dressed like this.'

And then, in front of the patients who were waiting for the doctor, she shouted, 'You're mad. Never come home again!'

The doctor came out to calm us down, but we'd already become a laughing stock. What really got me was her 'Never come home again.' That's my real concern, that they'll realise how poor I am and send me out like a dog, to run down my father's pension at their leisure. (Aunt Dionysia, who is always fair, had gone to her son in Paris and I had no one to back me up.)

Thankfully, the doctor took my side: 'Sweetheart, your brother wants the best for you.' She looked daggers at him and left in a huff.

I don't know where she went. I didn't have the strength to follow her anymore. I went to calm down in Agios Eleftherios Church, which had vespers.

I'm thinking about finding a room in Psyrri, to escape. I'd have my personal life, my icons, etc. It would be like an artist's studio. I'd do some preparation in case the palsy returned. I wouldn't completely leave my family home, or the two Megaeras would make mincemeat of my mother. I would go every day, but just to sleep and check on her health. In ten or fifteen years, when the poor thing will be at peace, I will go and find a cell on the Holy Mountain and see out the rest of my days.

I have no time to myself at all. I'm busy all day long, and I pray to God that I find a job and hold it down. Lighten my debts a bit. Before my time comes, I want to put on a habit and go to the Holy Mountain, to a beautiful and quiet skete.[2] I see the monk's habit as a

---

[2] A small monastery.

kind of deliverance from those people who call themselves my family. I would have my cell, my peace, and live at last like a human being. A man, as we all know, needs his peace after sixty. Unfortunately, I have lost many years—I was under the exploitation of immoral women and hateful employers. I was luckless.

My big sister has been pestering me to go to a notary and sell our house. Apparently, she's overcome with kindness now and wants us, 'for our parents' health', to move back to our village. Merely from this, it seems that she's overflowing with loans and is trying to escape by selling the house and kicking me out. When I repeatedly and stubbornly refused, she said, 'You're possessed. You have eight demons in you. Get a priest to exorcise you, you money-grubber—when you're dead there's no saving money!'

'You'll be the death of me, you two!' I said and stormed out. As I walked down the road in the frost, I started crying. I couldn't stop.

My father sticks up for them. 'If you don't help them, who will? A stranger?'

'Father, when you're ill, I'm at your side. Where are they? I'm always running around for you and mother and for that cow of a little sister. I even went to England for her.'

But he was unswayed: 'You must help them. I cannot.' Well, where can I get the money from? Should I become a thief? (He doesn't know what happened at work.) Whose fault is it that when he was in the army he squandered it all and now doesn't have a cent?

When I was young he wouldn't give me a drachma, even though all his friends had a great time on his tab. He threw it all at whores. (It's common knowledge that a drunkard wants a woman before he gets drunk.) He did this his whole life, before getting Parkinson's. Since then I've been always at his side, but I never once heard a 'thank you'.

He didn't let me become a priest—my dream—nor let me study. He sent me to work from when I was little, to bring money home.

Then he began to pressure me into going to the Permanent Commissioned Officers School. I did it for him, but I couldn't take it. I left after ten days. Then, when I returned after my military service, he told me to open a business of our own. He had just been dismissed. We opened a small studio. I worked like a Trojan from the early morning until night, and on the weekends I had a job at Mr P.'s printers. Dad played the boss: he only gave orders. That infuriated me, as I both rented the place and bought the machinery. I spent all my savings. He didn't pay one drachma. Even when I was in dire straits and couldn't pay the insurance contributions, he didn't help me, though he could have— I knew that. I was forced, therefore, to sell the machinery and get out of debt. And on the day of the trial by the insurance body (who I owed money to), he came into the public gallery and laughed at me, because I mixed things up a bit, from my fear and anxiety (it was my first time in court, and I was the accused).

Then came his brain trouble. Only then did he calm down. And I put everything to one side. He brought me into the world, after all. Honour your father, says the Commandment... Then came his accident and I was terrified we'd lose him. Later they diagnosed the Parkinson's and began treatment. I was told that all his organs had been destroyed by drink.

Sometimes, even if I'm just at home for a little, I forget myself and pick up the phone and it's the bank. A couple of days ago some bitch called me and said the usual stuff.

'I can't, I've got diabetes, certified by the doctor. I've also had palsy...'

'That is of no concern to us. We have people with cancer who pay their instalments.'

'The shame!' I screamed and slammed the phone down.

Right away she called back, and, idiot that I am, I picked it up.

'You can talk about it with our lawyers. Prison is also an option...' And she hung up.

I called a lawyer friend immediately.

'Essentially, they can't send you to prison.'

'Are you sure?'

'Prison is out of the question because of your illness. But you'll pay the debts. The same goes for your sisters. I think they're getting the same pressure from the banks but hiding it from you. You need to discuss it, no question. You're in danger of losing your house… All three of you have great responsibility.'

After all this, can I stay at home? I take the bus to the city centre, get off at Omonia Square and from there quickly on to Syntagma Square, Monastiraki, Plaka, Thiseio. I have no money to go to an internet café, as I used to. Now that I am unemployed again, I could go on various job websites—consultancies, in particular—and try to get hired. All the right bosses go to those sites to find employees with degrees, experience and specialised qualities.

I have looked deeply into how much an employee costs a business and I would like to promote a Greek workforce, which is in steep decline.

I return home after midnight, when everyone is asleep. Even my mother doesn't stay awake for me anymore. I eat alone, watch TV and at some point, about two, I go to bed. But I cannot sleep. The Furies come. Why aren't I working? Why do I have debts? Why don't I have a job of my own? Why will no woman come near me?

Friends have disappeared. They're afraid I'll ask for loans. There are a few (two or three, to be honest) who offer to buy me drinks, etc., but—I see it in their eyes—it's from pity. All this hurts me a lot. There's one thing I don't ever want to be called: a scrounger.

I didn't have a great life when I was little. I had no friends—my parents didn't allow it. They would say, 'Stay away from friends. You don't want them leading you astray.'

When I was six, we went as a family to Salamis for a swim. While the others went into the sea, I ran off and without realising it, ended up a kilometre away, in a playground full of children. My mother was worried. She sent my father to look for me. I saw him coming over, irate.

'Now you're in for it.'

He took me, kicking me all the way, back to the beach. He beat me again when we got home.

That roughened me up. I started breaking my toys, slingshotting the light bulbs, chopping up the plants in the pots, kicking cats in the street—to get a rise, probably. I suffered serious beatings. Mother grabbed the cooking spoons and hit me mercilessly. I hid them from her and she beat me again to give them back. In the evening when father came home she would tell him everything in great detail and there would be more. (Since then I've loved wooden spoons. They break, unlike the metal ones, which tear up your skin.)

I can't sit in peace. I don't know where this is all heading. I prefer the centre of Athens: I feel freer there. I don't want to be close to home, in Ethnikis Antistasis Square. It's full of Albanians. If I had my own home I would definitely sell it. Anyway, that's the politics of the Albanian: to make us leave our homes. It's an organised plot. They want to earn in two years what the Greeks achieved in thirty. That's what the commissar has learned, Alia's driver, to bag a Mercedes in twenty-four hours, and he thinks he'll manage the same in Greece. We need to keep strong.

In the apartment block where my aunt lives just up the road from us, they close the door at ten and don't open it to anyone. Not even me. It's a big apartment block and these places are flooded with Albanians and Romanians. If an old woman, a tenant, goes in and opens up with the key, how will she shove the Albanian out? She can't. She can't even speak. She knows that he might kill her.

He's been cantankerous all his life and made a fool of us everywhere. He thought his uniform gave him authority. One night he came home drunk again, and my mother rushed to lock the outer door. He began to kick it and swear. Suddenly he quieted down and we heard scratching at the lock. He was trying to force the door. My big sister notified the police. I remember holding my little sister in my arms, as she cried.

There was swearing and kicking from outside again. The emergency services came and my mother unlocked. Then we all saw the knife in his hands. He must have taken it from the taverna. The police respected him, even though we often had these episodes. The army and police are one.

'Until now we haven't logged the incidents in our books. But this time, there's the knife…' one of them said. The other added, 'Why are you putting us in this difficult position? Drunkenness is one thing, a knife is another…'

He listened with his head bowed. And when the policemen sat him down to talk, with mother and the rest of us in a corner, he fell asleep and started snoring.

Those two whores are the blight in our home. The older is arrogant and selfish—she reminds me of Old Nick's wife. I mean, as if she's some kind of fancy aristocrat, and we're all indebted to her. She works as a school teacher. She doesn't go every day, she goes whenever she feels like it. She's found two or three doctors of various specialisations and they give her notes to justify her absences.

I don't think she'll become a headmistress or achieve any position of responsibility. She's supposedly also doing a doctorate in philosophy. It's dragged on for five years now. She's got a stack of books on her desk, but she doesn't even open them. The other day when I asked her, she said she was studying Heraclitus. Let's believe it.

I didn't like state school at all, as the intellectual level was very low. We're talking about sodomites' kids. When the chap is fawning all day on the woman next-door or blaspheming continually, what will become of his child? I wanted to go back to private school, but with my father's excesses there wasn't the money.

My life was made unliveable as I was slightly portly. They stole my things, boxed my ears—where they knew I was sensitive—slandered me, insulted me. 'Chryso-valantis wears white pants and diarrhoea comes out of his bum!' The bigger lads would surround me in the playground so the teachers wouldn't see. 'Show us your dick, fatty,' they would say and laugh. I didn't say anything, I hung my head and took to my heels. Yes.

Even the teachers were merciless. Since they couldn't keep check of the rogues, they would explode at poor, defenceless Chrysovalantis three or four times a day. That's why they always made me sit at the front.

I was a very average pupil, always distracted. I couldn't control that, as much as I tried. One word from the teacher, one chance word, was enough to set me off on my fairy-tale, daydreaming journeys. And I didn't study. I couldn't study at home—it was always full of people and there was a whole load of problems: ill grandmothers, father with his drunkenness and shouting, mother with her pills (always out of it), my little sister back and forth to hospitals. Therefore, I went through all of primary school without study-ing—and I paid for it. I only excelled in Sunday School. Yes.

All my useless uncles dumped their family problems on us. They were always bringing my grandma

Chrysovalantia from the village and leaving her with us. Once I remember that I hadn't spoken nicely to her and I cried from guilt. It was a night when the poor thing couldn't sleep—she had trouble breathing—and she kept me awake telling me stories from her youth: how, she said, all the village lads were in love with her. 'I was rather a hit,' she said, and I started shouting because my eyes were closing from exhaustion.

It's well known that old people go mad for no apparent reason. Grandma was always fussing over her children in the village. They'd got her off their backs sharpish, and she would say, 'How's Vangelis getting on with the work on the house? Is Stathis taking his pills? Did Nikolas win his case? Did they plough? Sow? Reap?'

From morning till night, the same old. Always huffing and puffing. It was like we didn't exist. She would look at my mother, shake her head and say, 'Useless.'

I couldn't bear it. Once I yanked her sheets and started shouting, 'Stop, stop, stop! If you don't like it here, go to your sons… But they don't want you…!'

(I've confessed about that.)

One day, I don't remember exactly what I had done—I'd probably broken a plate—my mother beat me black and blue. It was over the top. I couldn't study in the state I was in, and I went to school in tears. The teacher thought that I did it on purpose to get out of class, so he took the long cane and beat me too. I sat, silent and bruised, at my desk, and when the bell rang for break I went out into the playground and began to do pull-ups manically. In the end I fell off and broke my left arm. I was in terrible pain but didn't shed a tear. A strange calmness overcame me. A sense of relief. As if I was pleased that no one would be able to beat me for a while.

The headmaster took me to hospital. They put my arm in plaster. I liked that a lot. He accompanied me home, and when my mother saw me, she took me in her arms and we started crying. We couldn't stop.

When a woman is in debt, her period doesn't stop—but when a man is in debt, he can't get it up. Unfortunately.

I don't tell them this at home because I don't want to embitter them, but I feel as if I'm the bastard son of my father. At one point he had five houses and I didn't even have the money for my insurance contributions. Still, any ill he did me I repaid with good.

And of course, I won't be falling back into Roro's trap, nor Eumorphia's, nor any other cunning woman's. It's been a long while since I've been caught up in whoredom.

A Russian woman came some time ago and whined:

'I have nothing, I don't know what to do. I'll kill myself to get some peace.'

'Do you want company? The funeral will work out cheaper...' I replied. She disappeared.

Since my big sister broke her leg, I do everything myself. I've become exhausted. But I believe that God will grant to my family to find its old self.

When I was about twelve, a family from Pyrgos in Eleia moved opposite us. The father, a complete crook, worked somewhere as a marble cutter. The son was a pest and the mother a brunette, unkempt, thick-lipped, absolutely for the loony-bin. She waged war on us. She was jealous of my mother's beauty. There was always some pretext: the rubbish, the water, etc., etc. She woke the whole neighbourhood with her shouting, threats and swearing. My mother was passive: she didn't speak or react. (She's the same way now.) But this situation affected us. A silence fell upon our hearts.

The madwoman was dowsing her patio when she saw my mother. She grabbed the hose and squirted water furiously at our windows. My mother came out and said politely, 'Why are you doing this?' Unperturbed, she retreated into her house and blasted out some Theodorakis songs.

Once, she caught my father in his uniform and said sharply, 'Collaborator!' My father stood on her doorstep, enraged. 'Say that again!' She locked herself in and didn't bother us for days.

Well, God punished her in the end: her husband got cancer and died in a month, in terrible pain. She stopped messing us around. She found a job as a cleaner, and when she saw that she couldn't make ends meet, she took her son and returned to their village.

When I was fourteen, something else happened.

A block down the road from us there was a framer's shop. A man from Corfu owned it, who was also a painter. He would paint ships, boats and seascapes. He was a friend of my father's. I would often go and he would teach me to paint at the back of his shop, where he had his workshop.

One day he said to me, 'At your age you need to be with a woman. I'll find you a nice one.'

From then on he would say it again and again, grinning. I was embarrassed and afraid of sinning, but I listened with some pleasure. It felt like he was tickling me.

One afternoon when we were in his workshop, he started telling me about women and gave me some Mavrodaphne to drink. 'It's good, isn't it? Let's have another.'

At the third glass he started caressing my genitals. I said to myself, 'Now he's going to rape me.' I froze, my mind went hazy and I began to cry.

'Calm down, laddie,' he drawled, but I leapt up from the chair, shouting 'Get off me!' and ran for the door. It was locked, and I banged on the windows but no one was passing by. I grabbed some wood for making frames and screamed amid my sobs, 'Get out, get out! I'll hit you!' He took fright, and to sweeten me he pulled out some money from his pocket, trembling. 'Here! Take this and go.'

At last he unlocked the door. I emerged, panting, and shot home like a bullet. Along with the shame, I was worried that my parents might get wind of it. My father in particular. I didn't want to cause him trouble, but I was also afraid of the Corfiot, who was sly and would say I was mad—it would all be a colossal nuisance.

In my childhood I was wounded a lot by my first confessor—he beat me. He would beat me when I had done something wrong and I mentioned it to him in confession. He dragged me brutally by the ear in front of my mother and she didn't dare say anything to him. I think that all those who work in psychology or spirituality are the worst; they don't forgive easily. These people wouldn't let me feel tenderness and love in my childhood. That's why I've now taken them down from the pedestal of respect and admiration on which I once held them.

That confessor sent me to a mathematician to give me private lessons—I always failed maths. I didn't study much, it's true, so the mathematician smacked me often. His wife (a hideous creature from Thessaloniki) complained to him, 'Why don't you get rid of him? He's taking it out of you. Don't you see that he can't cut it?' He punished me by making me write the same exercise fifty times. I felt useless.

From then on, my brain started growing tired. That's why I began eating too much. I always was, in any case, a rather portly lad who liked his grub.

As well as my confessor, the metropolitan also behaved unpredictably towards me. He would insult me in front of everyone (once even in a service) and then say, 'Chrysovalantis is very dear to me—he is a pure and good-natured lad.' Then he immediately found another excuse to bring me down. He asked, for example, 'What lovely food did we have for lunch today?'

'Lentils without oil.'

'Come on, you great fibber, who are you kidding?' And he looked me up and down, then at my belly and said, 'You think I can't see? All this fasting will be the death of you!' and everyone burst out laughing.

Unfortunately this is the norm in ecclesiastical circles. There is a kind of covert sadism and spiritual compulsion which leads to a complete shattering of the self and of dignity. And then they do whatever they want with you and you become their slave forever. They do that to so many. Many people I know have come a cropper. Thankfully they didn't manage with me. I'm a crafty little thing and I managed to escape them.

Two friends I told this to, who know the kinds of things that go on there, were amazed. 'Well done, Chrysovalantis, how did you manage not to go mad?'

Now after the palsy I feel very strange, even though it happened many years ago. I'm insecure. I want to see people, but I don't know if it's reciprocal. My mental state has taken a hit. I continually feel the need for more sleep and a deeper need for tenderness, love and real contact.

Grandma Chrysovalantia had lost it by the end.

She would ask everyone who came to our house, 'Can I take a photo of you?' And before they could reply, she would lift up her skirt and flash her knickers.

She did that to all our visitors without exception. We became a laughing stock—particularly if she'd managed to take her knickers off without mother seeing. Just imagine: we had priests, church committees, officers and their ladies visiting us then. (Of course, their children had a whale of a time with Grandma.)

In the end we stopped inviting people. Father was embarrassed about his mother and he would explode at Mother. She gave us a lot of trouble at the end, poor thing.

My fears have taken hold again! What if I take after my grandma? What if I have it in my genes? I shudder at the thought.

I don't use my briefcase anymore. I have everything I need (diaries, samplers, paper) in a simple plastic bag. I'm afraid I'll be robbed, what with all these junkies. And so many, so many foreigners. I'm scared.

Dirt, foreign dirt everywhere. On the buses, on the metro. They're everywhere, wherever you go, wherever you look. They've become a scourge, worse than the plagues of Egypt. I used to get out my perfumed hand-kerchiefs discreetly and hold them close to my nose, so I wouldn't faint from the stench, but now I've lost my inhibitions: I take out my bottle of cologne and spray it all around. Most people look at me askance, but why should I be ashamed? Let those who've become di-vorced from cleanliness feel ashamed.

I also have a bottle of rubbing alcohol with me at all times, to disinfect whatever I touch. I do the same to public toilets—of course, I try to avoid them like the devil avoids incense, but unfortunately I cannot, as I'm out of the house all day.

Yesterday as of eight thirty in the morning, the home phone started ringing. They didn't pick it up: both of them feigned indifference.

'Come on, girls, pick it up.'

No reply. I rushed out of the toilet to answer, but my big sister stopped me in the hall: 'Chrysovalantis, I've made an arrangement for my credit card debts.'

'How much do you owe?' I asked her, as we went into the kitchen for coffee.

She didn't reply immediately, she just brought in jam, butter and a cake. 'Here, try these, I made them,' she said with a smile, and I had the comforting sensa-tion that everything was alright.

'Two or three thousand?' I asked, after eating and having my coffee.

She looked at me, judging my reaction. 'Thirty-five thousand...' she murmured. I had a fit! 'How much?!' Crockery and cutlery flew out of my hands; my mouth went dry; I had to go to the toilet.

From outside the toilet door I heard, 'I've arranged eighty-eight instalments.'

I came out and looked at her, speechless. My little sister came over and they ushered me into the kitchen, closing the door so our parents wouldn't hear.

'Darling Chrysovalantis, it's for the two of us. It works out at four hundred euros a month... Do you think you could undertake the instalments?'

'As soon as the pension lump sum comes in, we'll pay you back,' added my big sister.

I felt like I was melting away. Something broke inside me. I heard myself breathing. I heard myself say, 'I've been unemployed a year and...' I left, head down, without a second glance.

I took to the streets. Out of the five properties, two are left to these sick women: one in each of their names. In any case, at some point the banks will mortgage one, if they don't keep the arrangement. My lawyer friend told me that. I don't mind what they do, as long as they leave me in peace. Enough is enough.

I'm living in a thriller. You see them everywhere. Everywhere. Albanians, Poles, Romanians, Hungarians,

Bulgarians, 'Macedonians', Montenegrins, Moldavians, Kurds, Pakistanis, Iranians, Iraqis, Indians, Filipinos, Chinese, Russians, Georgians, Ukrainians, Senegalese, Afghans, Somalis, Nigerians, Sudanese, Congolese, Tanzanians, Kenyans, Ethiopians, Indonesians, Bangladeshis, Dominicans, Moroccans, Nepalese, and, and, and…

It does my head in.

I wake up in the night in a white room, all alone. My head is pounding. Where am I? Who am I? Who are the others in the beds around me? Is the one opposite me dead?

Something is happening to my face. Muscle contraction. My eye pulls at my mouth, and my ear at my eye. I feel a shudder. The thin thread linking my soul to my body snaps. I see my soul coming out of my body and flying high, then even higher. Free. A sensation of velvet surrounds me. I sink.

In the morning a smiling, tasty nurse comes. I want to speak. I open my mouth and no sound emerges. What has happened this time? I look at her and cry dry tears. She takes blood, all smiles. Warm blood— the body-soul link. If blood cools, then the soul can't communicate with the body. I need to repent. This is God punishing me.

The second day, my mouth and eyes are even worse. Everything has a metallic taste. I see shadows in my dreams. Evil shadows.

'What day of the month is it?' I stutter.

'Ninth of December... you've been with us ten days.'

I look her in the eye, crying dry—very dry—tears.

'You'll be out tomorrow.'

I grasp the pity in her eyes.

I went back home.

If I had a degree, I would find a job even in my state: experience can't be discounted. I would rent a little flat in the city centre, to be master of myself. If the girls ever come, they'd be welcome—I don't hold grudges. I'm certain that the little one would come, even if in secret. She loves me a lot. Yes.

I went with my friend M. for coffee in a place near the Caravel Hotel. A lovely place, but I noticed that even here the waiters were foreigners. A strange fear came over me, I wanted us to get up and go. I became tense, I had the impression they had put something in our coffee. Poison?

I've often been to psychiatrists. They gave me pills to lower my blood pressure. Then they gave me antidepressants which did me good but caused me a lot of pain in my eyes: they stung, went blurry and I couldn't see properly. I also cried a lot, as I remembered everything I had been through, all the humiliation I had undergone. At some point the pills kicked in and I came round.

Before fourteen months had gone by, however, Eumorphia came into my life—alas—and she took me back to the glory days. I felt really, really humiliated again.

My big sister said the other day, 'I'll find some old fool to give me stability. I can't get by just on my wage and my rental income.'

Did I really hear that or was it my imagination? What will happen to our little sister then? I don't have the strength even to think about it.

I have only unpleasant memories from my childhood. I think that if I get a place of my own I will feel security and peace of mind. I will become slim and healthy. Yes.

I was turned into a broken piece of furniture. Everyone fought me on everything.

'You're not a good lad, you're not a good son, you're not a diligent pupil, you're a liar and a layabout.'

My childhood—a prison.

I went back. Home?

I've seen various incidents in hospitals. A woman screaming and running up and down in a strait jacket, as if possessed. They're chasing her and they can't catch her. She says, 'Go on, get lost, and your money, too, you cuckold. I prefer your pills to your money. Are you my father or Satan?' (Later I found out that she never knew her parents: she grew up with her grandmother.)

All this frightens me. Perhaps, I think, with everything I'm going through, I'll buckle, too. (I'm not made of stone.) I'll mess up, and then everyone will say, 'Is that the good-time boy Chrysovalantis, who once went out with tall, beautiful women and who is now unshaven, with grape-fungus growing on his face?'

What does the future hold? There is a great current of our fellow people being admitted to psychiatric units. I'm afraid that I'll go in as a tenant and become a permanent resident. Or perhaps I'll end up on some bench in Omonia Square with the drug addicts, stray animals and foreign prostitutes, begging just to get myself a piece of bread.

Is it better to be in or out of the psychiatric hospital? The scales tip towards the former: there's peace, security and the salvation of—in the words of the poet—'precious oblivion'.

Ten days.

I'm only thinking about my survival.

It's the first time in my life I've felt like this. I never believed that my virtuous sisters were in fact malicious elements of common penal law.

When you're down, bent double, they come and deal you a hammer-blow to the head to finish you off.

Ten. Days?

I wake up every day in a mess. My mind is confused. My weight aggravates the situation. There are days when I can't even stand up. My vision has also worsened—I don't see well anymore. Often, as I get up to go to the toilet, I feel that if I lose control a bit, I'll collapse. My heart palpitations are now permanent, as are my migraines. I'm heading straight for a heart attack or stroke. I carry a heavy, heavy burden.

I panic that third parties will come out of nowhere one fine morning, like paratrooper commandos, and wipe out everything I've built over my life.

I was away from home for ten days. And no one looked for me. No one.

I wake up at night and cry. My heart is a volcano, my eyes a well of tears. I always looked out for others. What about me?

I can't look at a woman. They all seem dirty. Rotten.

I'm afraid I'll sink someday. I'm scared. Scared.

But I am poor and needy: make haste unto me, O God: thou art my help and my deliverer; O Lord, make no tarrying.

Ten. Ten?

I have hypnophobia. I'm afraid to close my eyes—my heart beats like there's an earthquake. I wake up in a panic, my mind scattered. I sometimes fall out of bed. I feel constantly that my eyes are leaping out of their sockets. I'm very afraid of the slander that others, ill-wishers, can commit. For I represent a type of quiet and oppressed person who, since they go with their cross in hand, cannot protect themselves.

Home? Did I go back?

I'm afraid of slander. I'm afraid of temptation. I'm afraid of the dawning day. I'm afraid.

I hear murmurings from the kitchen as I go to the toilet. I don't drag my feet anymore, and I pee standing up again. The elastic of my pyjamas hurts a bit, but oh well.

'What shall we do with him?' Is it my big sister speaking? Do they know I'm next-door?

'As if it wasn't enough he's unemployed, he's gone and got ill again, the useless bugger.' That's definitely my little sister. Her too?

Her too.

I pull the flush deliberately. Enough. Enough!

I burrow myself under the covers.

I wake at six o'clock. I wash myself as well as possible, get dressed, put on my blue suit, my good tie and my cologne. It takes me over an hour.

I go to my bookcase and open the book where I have hidden my last fifty-euro note. I leave as quietly as I can.

The roads still have not livened up. The only people moving with purpose are a dozen refugees rushing onto the buses around Korydallos Square. I walk slowly. My legs are trembling. I struggle to stand properly. I look around. I hear my blood echoing around my body.

At last, the shops open. I go into the first: a gift shop. The saleswoman smiles at me.

'Gifts for two ladies,' I stutter.

'Of course. Let me show you…'

A nice scarf in sky-blue for my big sister. I look at the price-tag. Fifteen euros. Fine.

'Now something more expensive.'

She shows me a cabinet with gloves in. I choose a pair of red suede, the little one's favourite colour. I look at the price. Thirty-nine euros. I don't have enough. I take out my fifty-euro note.

'For such a polite gentleman I'll make a discount, considering the time of year.'

She wraps them in separate boxes and puts them in two bags with Christmas trees on. I shake her hand and make my way home. Slowly.

In my haste, I didn't take my pills. Walking is difficult, but it doesn't matter. Come on, old boy, you can do it. One more step... you're getting there.

Finally, I find myself outside our block. I look at it as if for the first time. It was once all ours. If the old lift has broken again, how will I make it to the fifth floor? I press the button. It's working. Thank you. Thank you.

Arriving upstairs, the smell of cooking beef hits me. I put the key in the door. There's a suitcase. Whose suitcase? There's a label on the handle. I pull it up and read it.

Right. OK.

I leave my gifts outside the door. I take my suitcase and leave.

For my days are consumed like smoke, and my bones are burned as an hearth. My heart is smitten, and withered like grass; so that I forget to eat my bread. By reason of the voice of my groaning my bones cleave to my skin. I am like a pelican of the wilderness: I am like an owl of the desert. I watch, and am as a sparrow alone upon the house top.

I board the bus to Omonia Square. I sit in the back seats. My pills. I open the suitcase. Ah, they forgot to put them in. I rest my head on the metal bar of the seat in front —to cool my mind.

'Last stop,' shouts someone. Did I fall asleep?

I drag myself to Stadiou Street. The suitcase tires me out. The trolley bus is full. Two kids look at me and giggle. I'm sweating. Do I smell?

I get off at Syntagma Square. I need the toilet. I go into a café. Straight to the toilet. The suitcase, where is the suitcase? It's gone, too.

On Ermou Street there are thousands of people. Faces. Teeth. Nails. Hubbub. Everything's blurred. I'm cold. Laughter. Shouts of wishes. What's the celebration? Voices. Smells. Balloons. Babies. The tourist train. Boat. Trumpets. Clowns.

The world has got smaller. It's shrunk. Shutters are down. Places are for rent.

I go up the cathedral steps. Slowly. Quiet. No one around. I kneel at the icon of Christ Pantocrator.

Peace.

I'm anxious. Very anxious. Agonised. Will I succeed? Will the Most Merciful give me strength? Will I cope? Chrysovalantis no longer—Maximus. Metropolitan Maximus of Thessaly and Fanariofarsala. I will minister to the flock of my beloved, ancestral land. My mouth has dried up. What emotion! I see the Archbishop of

Athens and All Greece—he's getting ready to ordain me. My hands are trembling. Will I succeed? Will I succeed? The cathedral is packed to the rafters. I see my parents, sisters, confessors, friends. What emotion! Behind them are cousins, acquaintances, neighbours, old bosses, Marinaki, Old Nick, Eumorphia, Roro, Claudia. They tell me that Mitropoleos Road is jammed with worshippers, from Syntagma to Plaka. Metropolitan of Thessaly and Fanariofarsala! Me! His Holiness nods. 'Welcome, Your Holiness... Excuse me? What? What did you say? Me for archbishop? You're... you're resigning? But why me? Worthless, insignificant, sinning me? It's a heavy, heavy burden. Your Holiness, I beg you, release me from this... There are so many shepherds, so many capable metropolitans... the Metropolitan of Mesogaia and Lavreotiki, of Polyani and Kilkis, of Sisani and Siatisti... Why me? Is it the will of the Lord? Is the Omnipotent asking me for obedience? Then... then... then Thy will be done.' My eyes tear up from emotion. So, is this why the luminaries of the Orthodox world are here? The Patriarchs of Alexandria, Jerusalem, Antioch, Russia, Serbia, Georgia, Romania, Bulgaria. The Archbishops of America, Australia, Cyprus, Poland, Albania, the Czech Republic and Slovakia. The president of the Holy Supervision of Mount Athos. To honour me? And behold! I see His Holiness the Patriarch himself coming over. What? What? I am speechless. He's going to ordain me! 'Your Holiness...' I stutter. I greet him with humility and respect. I incline my head. His Holiness puts on his mitre and hands over the pastoral staff. Then he says in a booming voice, 'Hail!' 'Hail!' chant the metropolitans, bishops, archimandrites and abbots. 'Hail!' go the cantors. 'Hail! Hail!' go Marinaki, Old Nick, Eumorphia, Roro and Claudia. 'Hail!' chants the whole church in unison. Hail! Hail! Hail! Hail! Hail! Hail! Hail! Hail! Hail! Hail! Hail, hail, hai, haihai-haihaihaaaaaaaaaaaaaaaaaaaaaaaaaaaaaaaaaaaaaaaaaaa aaaaaaaaaaaaaaaaaaaaaaaaaaaaaaaaaaaaaaaaaa

NOTES

All biblical quotations are from the King James Bible, unless otherwise indicated, with the exception of the book's epigraph.

p. 16   'A faithful friend is a strong defence: and he that hath found such an one hath found a treasure,' *Wisdom of Sirach* 6.14.

p. 20   Psalm 142:1-3.

p. 51   *Matthew* 21:31-32.

p. 54, 117   *Matthew* 27:64.

p. 71   Triodion, Kathisma Hymn of Holy Wednesday.

p. 83   'The Lord will abhor the bloody and deceitful man': Psalm 5:6.

p. 91   The Shepherd of Hermas, 32:1-2. (Translated by J.B. Lightfoot in *The Apostolic Fathers*, 1893).

p. 102   *Apostikha* (*Stikhera of Repentance*) from the service of Tuesday Matins.

p. 117, 151 '[God] will render to every man according to his deeds', *Romans* 2:6.

p. 146   'Lord, remember me when thou comest into thy kingdom', *Luke* 23:42.

p. 148   'Enter thou into the joy of thy lord', *Matthew* 25:21.

p. 163   *1 Corinthians* 7:8-9.

p. 193   'The rich have wanted...of any good.' Psalm 34:10 (*Douay-Rheims Bible*).

p. 199   *Great Orologion*, morning prayer.

p. 238   Psalm 70:5.

p. 240   Psalm 102:3-7.

MODERN
GREEK
CLASSICS

C.P. CAVAFY
Selected Poems
Translated by David Connolly

Cavafy is by far the most translated and well-known Greek poet internationally. Whether his subject matter is historical, philosophical or sensual, Cavafy's unique poetic voice is always recognizable by its ironical, suave, witty and world-weary tones.

ODYSSEUS ELYTIS
1979 NOBEL PRIZE FOR LITERATURE
In the Name of Luminosity and Transparency
With an Introduction by Dimitris Daskalopoulos

The poetry of Odysseus Elytis owes as much to the ancients and Byzantium as to the surrealists of the 1930s and the architecture of the Cyclades, bringing romantic modernism and structural experimentation to Greece. Collected here are the two speeches Elytis gave on his acceptance of the 1979 Nobel Prize for Literature.

M. KARAGATSIS
The Great Chimera
Translated by Patricia Felisa Barbeito

A psychological portrait of a young French woman, Marina, who marries a sailor and moves to the island of Syros, where she lives with her mother-in-law and becomes acquainted with the Greek way of life. Her fate grows entwined with that of the boats and when economic downturn arrives, it brings passion, life and death in its wake.

ANDREAS LASKARATOS

Reflections

BILINGUAL EDITION

Translated by Simon Darragh
With an Introduction by Yorgos Y. Alisandratos

Andreas Laskaratos was a writer and poet, a social thinker and, in many ways, a controversialist. His *Reflections* sets out, in a series of calm, clear and pithy aphorisms, his uncompromising and finely reasoned beliefs on morality, justice, personal conduct, power, tradition, religion and government.

ALEXANDROS PAPADIAMANDIS

Fey Folk

Translated by David Connolly

Alexandros Papadiamandis holds a special place in the history of Modern Greek letters, but also in the heart of the ordinary reader. *Fey Folk* follows the humble lives of quaint, simple-hearted folk living in accordance with centuries-old traditions and customs, described here with both reverence and humour.

ALEXANDROS RANGAVIS

The Notary

Translated by Simon Darragh

A mystery set on the island of Cephalonia on the eve of the Greek Revolution of 1821, this classic work of Rangavis is an iconic tale of suspense and intrigue, love and murder. *The Notary* is Modern Greek literature's contribution to the tradition of early crime fiction, alongside E.T.A. Hoffman, Edgar Allan Poe and Wilkie Collins.

ANTONIS SAMARAKIS
The Flaw
Translated by Simon Darragh

A man is seized from his afternoon drink at the Cafe Sport by two agents of the Regime by car toward Special Branch Headquarters, and the interrogation that undoubtedly awaits him there. Part thriller and part political satire, *The Flaw* has been translated into more than thirty languages.

GEORGE SEFERIS   BILINGUAL EDITION
1963 NOBEL PRIZE FOR LITERATURE
Novel and Other Poems
Translated by Roderick Beaton

Often compared during his lifetime to T.S. Eliot, George Seferis is noted for his spare, laconic, dense and allusive verse in the Modernist idiom of the first half of the twentieth century. Seferis better than any other writer expresses the dilemma experienced by his countrymen then and now: how to be at once Greek and modern.

ILIAS VENEZIS
Serenity
Translated by Joshua Barley

Inspired by the author's own experience of migration, the novel follows the journey of a group of Greek refugees from Asia Minor who settle in a village near Athens. It details the hatred of war, the love of nature that surrounds them, the hostility of their new neighbours and eventually their adaptation to a new life.

GEORGIOS VIZYENOS
Thracian Tales
Translated by Peter Mackridge

These short stories bring to life Vizyenos' native Thrace, a corner of Europe where Greece, Turkey and Bulgaria meet. Through masterful psychological portayals, each story keeps the reader in suspense to the very end: Where did Yorgis' grandfather travel on his only journey? What was Yorgis' mother's sin? Who was responsible for his brother's murder?

GEORGIOS VIZYENOS
Moskov Selim
Translated by Peter Mackridge

A novella by Georgios Vizyenos, one of Greece's best-loved writers, set in Thrace during the time of the Russo-Turkish War, whose outcome would decide the future of southeastern Europe. *Moskov Selim* is a moving tale of kinship, despite the gulf of nationality and religion.

NIKIFOROS VRETTAKOS   BILINGUAL EDITION
Selected Poems
Translated by David Connolly

The poems of Vrettakos are firmly rooted in the Greek landscape and coloured by the Greek light, yet their themes and sentiment are ecumenical. His poetry offers a vision of the paradise that the world could be, but it is also imbued with a deep and painful awareness of the dark abyss that the world threatens to become.

AN ANTHOLOGY BILINGUAL EDITION

Rebetika: Songs from the Old Greek Underworld

Edited and translated by Katharine Butterworth & Sara Schneider

The songs in this book are a sampling of the urban folk songs of Greece during the first half of the twentieth century. Often compared to American blues, rebetika songs are the creative expression of the *rebetes*, people living a marginal and often underworld existence on the fringes of established society.